Dearest Mokshi

New Enjoying Mathematics

Practice Book

With Mental Maths

With lots of Love from Thethe & Petti

BOOK 4

Aashalata Badami

OXFORD
UNIVERSITY PRESS

OXFORD
UNIVERSITY PRESS

Oxford University Press is a department of the University of Oxford.
It furthers the University's objective of excellence in research, scholarship, and education by publishing worldwide. Oxford is a registered trade mark of Oxford University Press in the UK and in certain other countries.

Published in India by
Oxford University Press
YMCA Library Building, 1 Jai Singh Road, New Delhi 110001, India

First published in 2011
Ninth impression 2015

ISBN-13: 978-0-19-806427-5
ISBN-10: 0-19-806427-6

Typeset in Times New Roman
by Manthan Technologies, New Delhi 110 034
Printed in India by Magic International (P) Ltd., Greater Noida

Illustrations by Manthan Technologies

Preface

Practice is one of the key factors needed to strengthen a child's understanding and application of a concept, especially in a subject such as Mathematics. An attempt is therefore made in the series, ***New Enjoying Mathematics Practice Books with Mental Maths,*** to approach each concept from different perspectives using simple language and keeping the guidelines of the NCF 2005 in view. Wherever possible, stress is laid on the practical aspects of the subject, with a large number of questions relating to the everyday experiences and interests of the pupils. A concerted effort has been made to make the practice aspect of mathematics education an interesting and motivating one—an experience that the child looks forward to and enjoys. The series also includes a number of worksheets which emphasize both the development of problem-solving skills and the linking of mathematics to the real world.

Key Features

- Carefully graded, topic-specific *Practice Worksheets* as part of essential drill work
- *Mental Maths Worksheets* to sharpen the mathematical skills
- *Activity-Based Worksheets* for better understanding of concepts
- *Subject-Integration Worksheets*
- *Problem-Solving Worksheets*
- *Real-Life Application Worksheets*
- *Higher Order Thinking Skills Questions (HOTS)*
- *Self-Correcting Worksheets*
- *Multiple Choice Questions*

The last two also lend themselves to Formative and Summative Assessments should the teacher choose to use them in that manner. The self-correcting worksheets help students spot errors, if any, and correct them on their own. Multiple choice questions are consistently provided to make the students revisit the previously learned skills. Some assessment ideas have also been incorporated for use in the classroom.

The symbols FA and SA are being used to highlight the pages which can be used for Formative and Summative Assessments respectively.

We trust that the teachers will find the suggestions given in this book useful and the students will find it interesting and exciting to use.

Thanks are due to the editorial, sales and marketing teams of OUP who continue, year after year, to amaze me with their dedication. My special thanks also goes out to countless teachers who have given their support and valuable feedback time and again. I thank my family for their limitless patience, and, above all, my never-ending gratitude for the blessings that I have received from above.

Aashalata Badami

CONTENTS

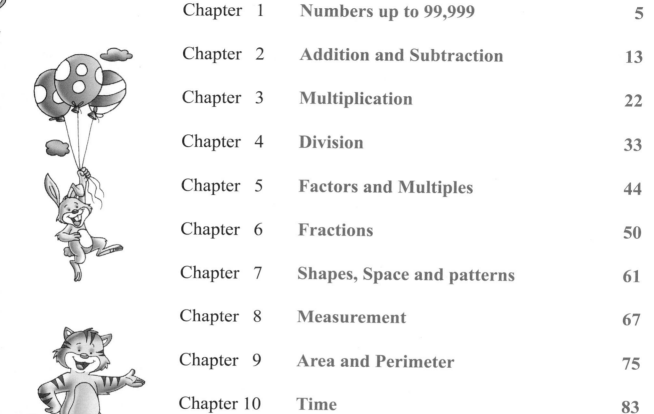

Numbers up to 99,999

1

SKIP COUNTING

Which fish has each fisherman caught?

- Use a red pencil to join the dots. Start at 8460. Count in tens.
- Use a green pencil to join the dots. Start at 10,560. Count in hundreds.
- Use a blue pencil to join the dots. Start at 63,080. Count in thousands.

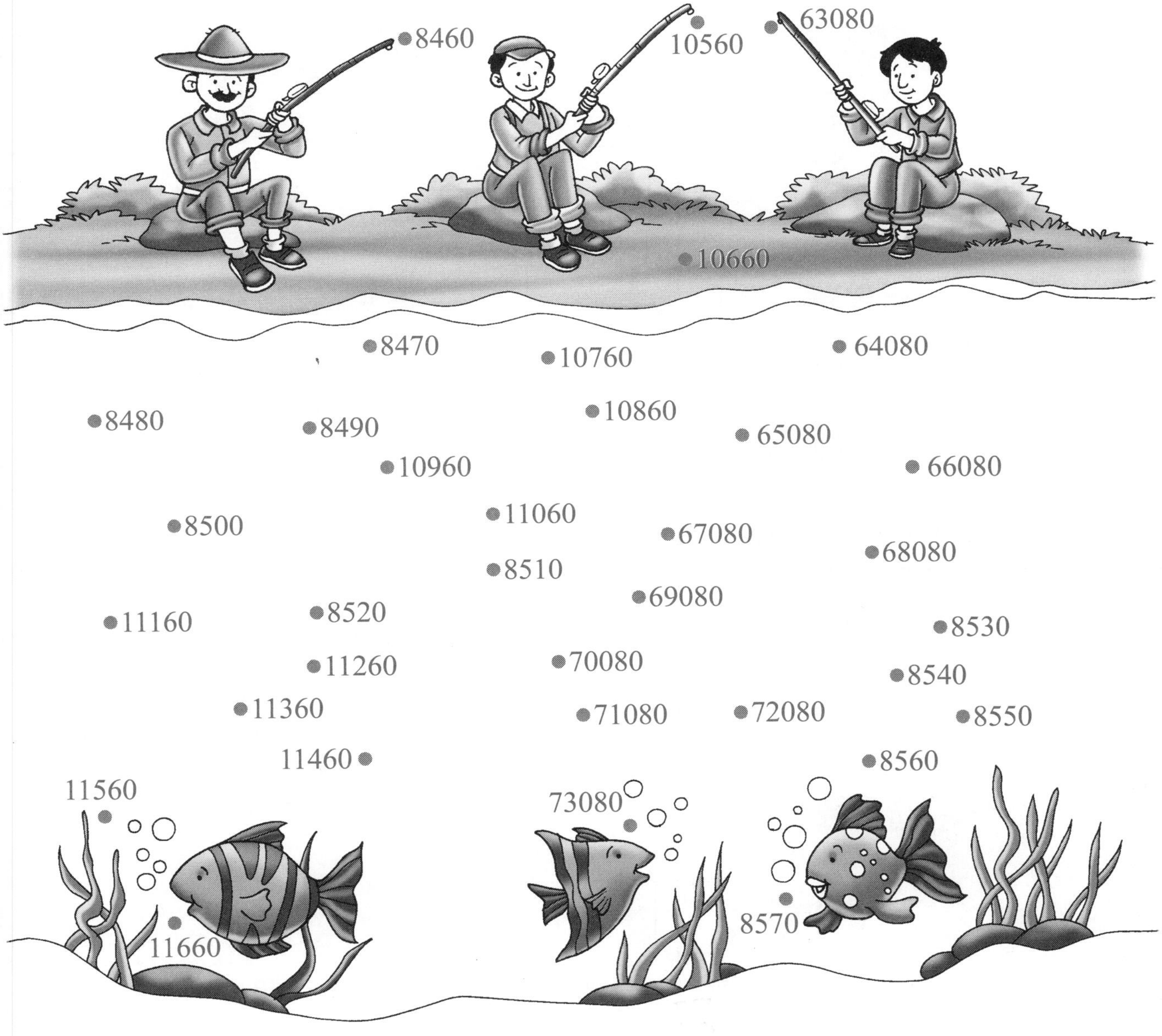

5-AND 6-DIGIT NUMBERS

Rajul and Meera are playing a game where points are calculated according to the place where the beads fall on the game board.

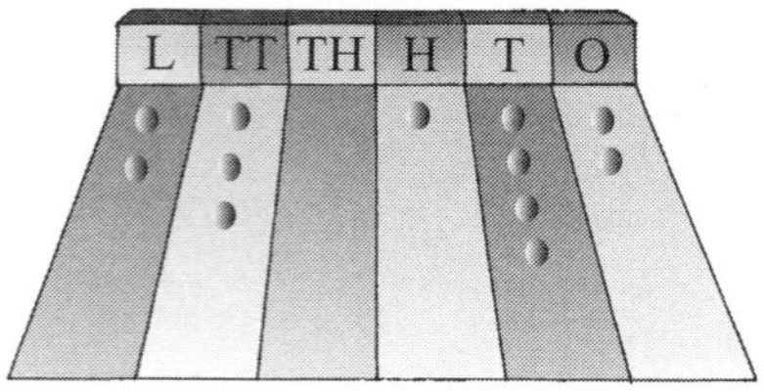

This shows the number 230142 and is written in words as 'two lakh thirty thousand one hundred forty-two'.

Write the number shown by each game board. Compare by using > or < in the box.

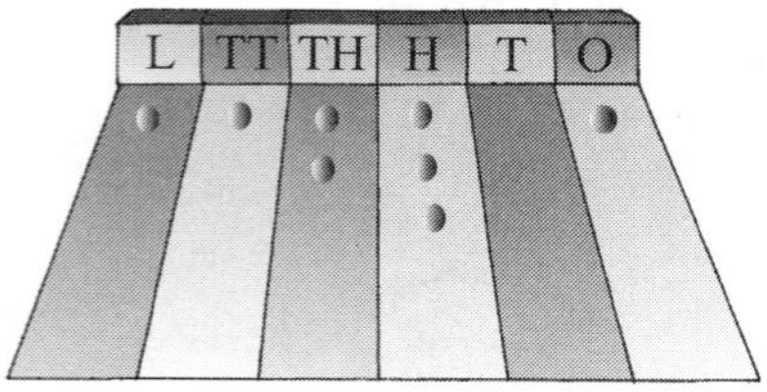

______________ ☐ ______________

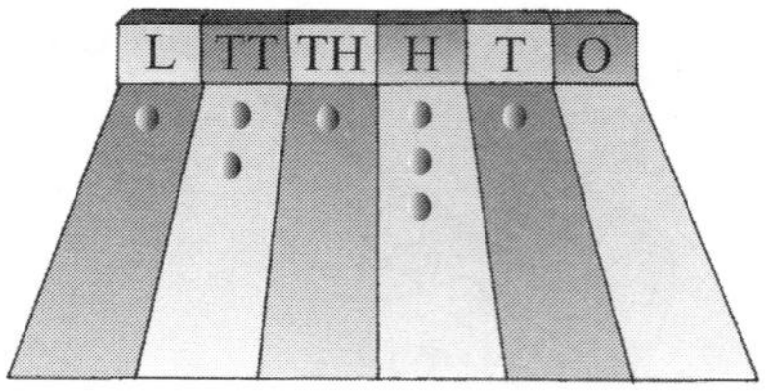

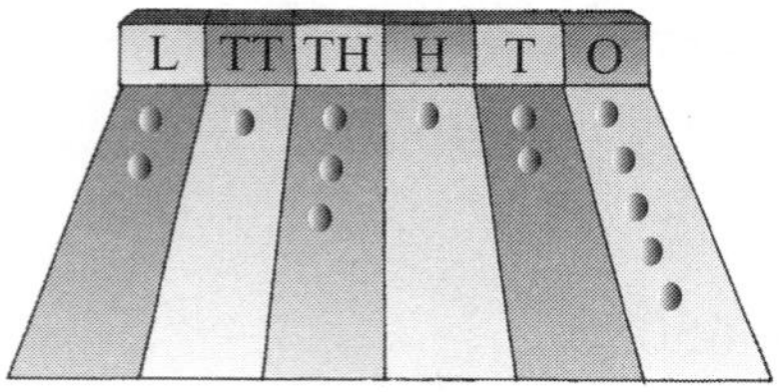

______________ ☐ ______________

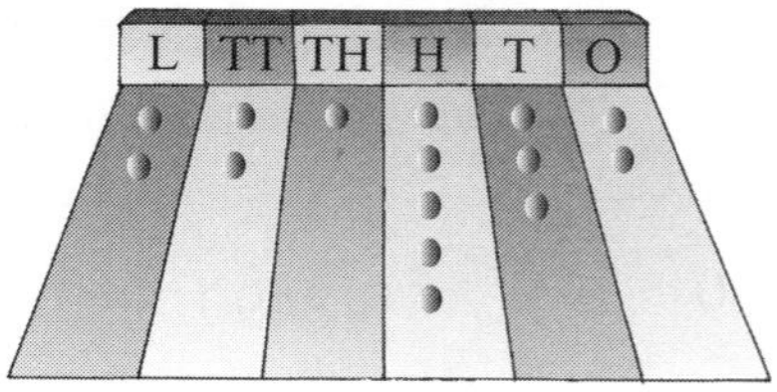

Draw the beads to show the scores. Put > or < in the box.

26341

☐

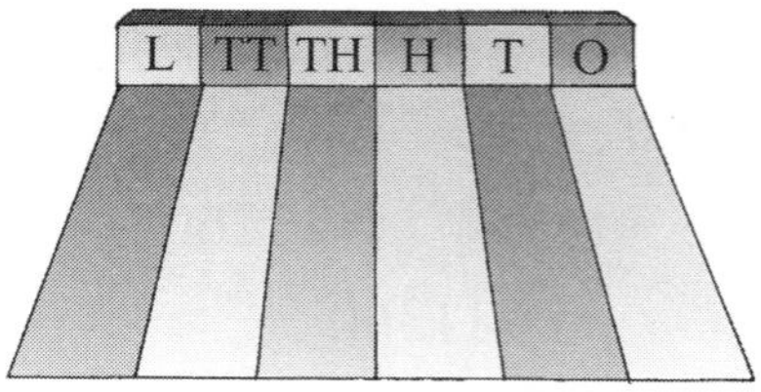

23461

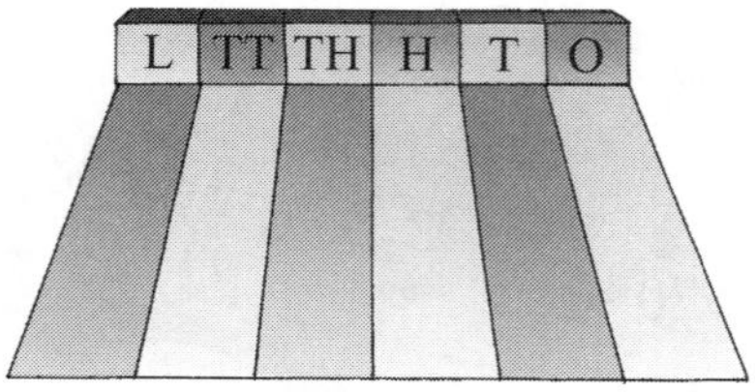

120706

☐

102760

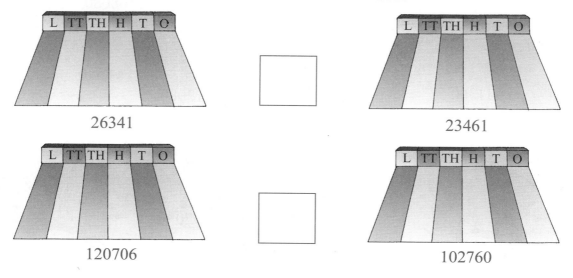

NUMBER NAMES

WHAT WAS THE OFFICIAL MOTTO OF THE XIX COMMONWEALTH GAMES HELD IN OCTOBER 2010 AT DELHI?

This worksheet integrates Mathematics and General Knowledge.

Write in figures. Then match the corresponding letters to the number below to find the answer. One has been done for you.

Four lakh thirty-eight thousand forty	________	A
Twenty thousand three hundred sixty-seven	________	D
Ninety-eight thousand one hundred ninety	________	L
One lakh eighty-one thousand	1,81,000	C
Seventy-five thousand five	________	E
Four lakh thirty-eight thousand one hundred fourteen	________	N
Ninety-eight thousand one hundred nineteen	________	O
One lakh eighteen	________	P
Seventy-five thousand five hundred	________	T
Twenty-one thousand three hundred seventy-six	________	U
One lakh eighteen thousand	________	Y
Four lakh eighty-three thousand fourteen	________	M

C ___ ___ ___   ___ ___ ___

181000 98119 483014 75005   98119 21376 75500

___ ___ ___   ___ ___ ___ ___

438040 438114 20367   100018 98190 438040 118000

BUILDING NUMBERS

Use the digits to build numbers. Repeat the digits when required.

(a) 2 5 1 7 9

97521 — greatest number

smallest number

(b) 3 8 0 6 2

greatest number

smallest number

(c) 6 8 1 7

greatest 5-digit number

smallest 5-digit number

(d) 2 3 0 5

greatest 5-digit number

smallest 5-digit number

(e) 5 7 3

greatest 4-digit number

smallest 4-digit number

(f) 2 8 0

greatest 4-digit number

smallest 4-digit number

(g) 4 2 9

greatest 5-digit number

smallest 5-digit number

(h) 9 0 8

greatest 5-digit number

smallest 5-digit number

QUIZ !

SELF-CORRECTING WORKSHEET

Answer the questions. Find the answers in the boxes below and shade them to find an important digit in the place value concept.

1. Give the number that comes after 20999. ____________
2. Give the number before 104000. ____________
3. What number has 6 ten thousands, 4 hundreds and 3 ones? ____________
4. In the number 764135, what is the value of 7? ____________
5. Which is greater—82161 or 82116? ____________
6. Which is smaller—109110 or 109101? ____________
7. Which is the greatest number— 46191, 46119 or 46901? ____________
8. What number comes between 100179 and 100181? ____________
9. Give one number for 10000 + 5000 + 20. ____________
10. What number is 100 more than 23098? ____________
11. What number is 100 less than 900000? ____________
12. What number is 1000 less than 761876? ____________
13. Build the biggest 5-digit number using 2, 3, 7, 6, 4. ____________
14. Round 35465 to the nearest 100. ____________
15. Build the smallest number using 0, 1, 2, 3, 8. ____________
16. Round 343876 to the nearest 1000. ____________

21000	**344000**	**46901**	**76432**	**109101**
15020	**111020**	**22354**	**35600**	**700000**
82161	**99000**	**43169**	**54928**	**100180**
760876	**88080**	**76000**	**76700**	**899900**
10238	**35500**	**60403**	**23198**	**103999**

ROMAN NUMERALS

SELF-CORRECTING WORKSHEET

First multiply. Then write the product in Roman Numerals on the cross-number puzzle below using the clues across and down.

Clues Across

(a) 29 × 1 =

(d) 5 × 6 =

(g) 11 × 1 =

(h) 4 × 4 =

(j) 3 × 9 =

(m) 11 × 2 =

(n) 4 × 5 =

(o) 3 × 4 =

Clues Down

(b) 2 × 19 =

(c) 7 × 3 =

(e) 13 × 2 =

(f) 2 × 2 =

(i) 4 × 9 =

(k) 3 × 3 =

(l) 5 × 1 =

(j) 2 × 5 =

	a	b		c		d		e	
f								g	
		h				i			
					j				
k				l					
m								n	
					o				

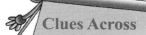

HIGHER ORDER THINKING SKILLS

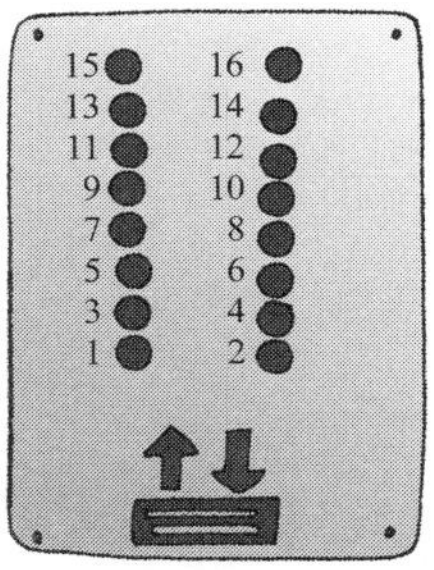

1. Mini got on to the lift on the 10th floor. She went down 3 floors, and then went up 7 floors. Again, she went down 5 floors and then went up 1 floor and got out. What floor did she finally get out on?

____

2. Four fishes are in a fish tank. Some are golden and some are white in colour. Show all the different combinations that are possible of the fishes.

____

3. A road has houses numbered from 11 to 151. On the left are the odd number houses and on the right are the even number houses. How many houses are there on the left of the road?

____

4. Two friends made Teacher's Day cards together. They made 18 cards. Both made a different number of cards. Both made less than 11 cards and one made more than 9 cards. How many cards did each make?

____

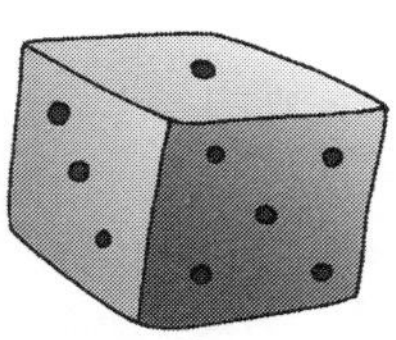

5. The opposite sides of a die add up to 7. What is the largest total possible if you can see only three sides at a time? What is the smallest total?

____

MENTAL MATHS

1. Make the biggest 5-digit number using 3, 1, 6, 7, 0. __________
2. What is the Roman Numeral for 34? __________
3. Round 3478 to the nearest 10. __________
4. Give the expanded notation for 12805. __________
5. 4 ten thousands + 5 thousands + 3 tens ☐ 45030. (Use >, < or =)
6. What is the value of the digit 8 in the number 812765? __________
7. Rearrange 23654, 23645, 230675 and 230965 in ascending order. __________
8. Make the smallest 5-digit number using 1, 5, 3, 0, 9. __________
9. Give one number for 300000 + 400 + 9. __________
10. Count in ten thousands: 58752, 68752, __________, __________, __________, __________
11. What does the digit 7 stand for in the number 27598? ______
12. Give the sum of the place values of 3 in the number 43833. ______
13. Make the largest 5-digit number possible with 3, 6, 1. __________
14. Round 38764 off to the nearest 100. __________
15. Round 140987 off to the nearest 1000. __________
16. Count in hundreds: 13457, 13567 __________, __________, __________, __________.
17. Rearrange 34742, 34765, 24876, 24537 in descending order. __________
18. 93576 ☐ 93559 (Use >, <, or =)
19. Count in thousands: 27590, 28590, __________, __________, __________, __________
20. 99234 ☐ 111234 (Use >, <, or =)

Students may do only 10 sums at a time.

Addition and Subtraction

2

ADDITION

Add. Regroup when required.

1. 9413 + 267	2. 5034 + 398	3. 2694 + 540	4. 9279 + 526
5. 8325 + 1567	6. 7156 + 2321	7. 8213 + 6543	8. 7852 + 2976
9. 25270 + 8763	10. 64273 + 5291	11. 85431 + 6752	12. 36347 + 8384
13. 43816 + 15421	14. 25424 + 29836	15. 16953 + 37638	16. 78062 + 15746
17. 9511, 1605 + 2914	18. 5678, 845 + 7620	19. 19395, 2319 + 56489	20. 27503, 12356 + 35401

SUBTRACTION

PRACTICE WORKSHEET

Subtract. Regroup when required.

1. $5216 - 376$
2. $6545 - 898$
3. $3657 - 245$
4. $8971 - 980$
5. $9327 - 2105$
6. $7414 - 3292$
7. $6763 - 4367$
8. $4889 - 2458$
9. $5000 - 1234$
10. $6001 - 4322$
11. $7010 - 3965$
12. $8100 - 7263$
13. $92135 - 1563$
14. $65657 - 2416$
15. $56778 - 3989$
16. $25599 - 5639$
17. $83212 - 23593$
18. $74524 - 44012$
19. $43846 - 15986$
20. $37368 - 25687$
21. $17302 - 4621$
22. $78001 - 53905$
23. $69010 - 32654$
24. $55000 - 39684$

MIXED PRACTICE

WHAT WAS THE IMPERIAL LIBRARY IN KOLKATA CALLED AFTER INDEPENDENCE?

To find the answer, first find each sum or difference. Use the decoder to find the letter that matches the answer. Then write the matching letter in the space below.

28999 +36236 = 65235 T	3784 +6900 =	81925 +5836 =

This worksheet integrates Mathematics with General Knowledge.

12561 +33655 =	8596 +13088 =	56249 +8986 =	2546 +540 =	36029 +16500 =	8997 +37219 =	11392 +10292 =	5236 +8998 =

16801 −2567 =	7648 −4562 =	7010 −2384 =	11320 −8510 =	72871 −51187 =	12322 −9512 =	30001 −17215 =

,

11407 −8321 =	51413 −5197 =	51000 −26583 =	9878 −6792 =	26910 −5226 =

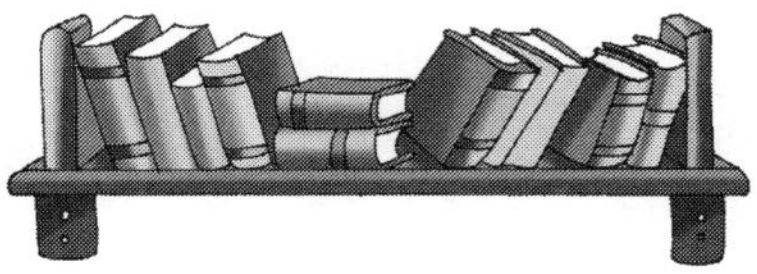

Decoder

21684 - A	4626 - B	24417 - D	87761 - E
10684 - H	3086 - I	14234 - L	46216 - N
52529 - O	2810 - R	65235 - T	12786 - Y

MENTAL MATHS

USING COMPENSATION TO ADD

Change to multiples of 10 or 100 to add mentally.

$$\begin{array}{r} 38 \\ +56 \\ \hline ? \end{array}$$

$38 + 2 = 40$
$56 - 2 = 54$
94

$$\begin{array}{r} 155 \\ +198 \\ \hline ? \end{array}$$

$155 - 2 = 153$
$198 + 2 = 200$
353

Change the first number to a multiple of 10

1. 78 + 17 = ____
2. 28 + 77 = ____
3. 58 + 23 = ____
4. 47 + 48 = ____
5. 61 + 53 = ____
6. 82 + 52 = ____

Change the second number to a multiple of 10

7. 24 + 39 = ____
8. 62 + 51 = ____
9. 32 + 38 = ____
10. 45 + 57 = ____
11. 24 + 76 = ____
12. 55 + 22 = ____

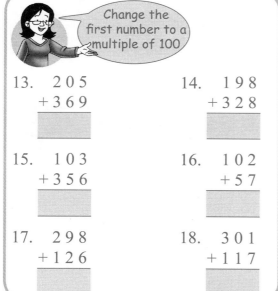

Change the first number to a multiple of 100

13. 205 + 369 = ____
14. 198 + 328 = ____
15. 103 + 356 = ____
16. 102 + 57 = ____
17. 298 + 126 = ____
18. 301 + 117 = ____

Change the second number to a multiple of 100

19. 187 + 297 = ____
20. 246 + 102 = ____
21. 168 + 201 = ____
22. 373 + 202 = ____
23. 184 + 198 = ____
24. 477 + 197 = ____

In addition, increase one number and decrease the other by the same amount.

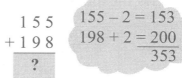

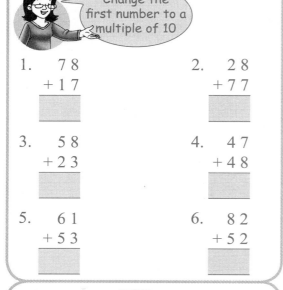

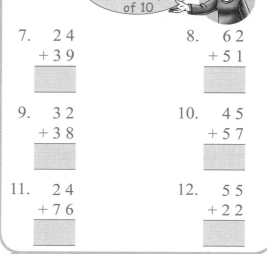

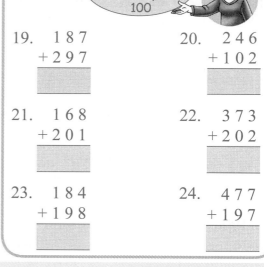

MENTAL MATHS

USING COMPENSATION TO SUBTRACT

Change to multiples of 10 or 100 to subtract mentally.

$$\begin{array}{r} 65 \\ -\,38 \\ \hline ? \end{array} \qquad \begin{array}{l} 65 + 2 = \;\; 67 \\ 38 + 2 = -\,40 \\ \hline \qquad\quad\;\; 27 \end{array}$$

$$\begin{array}{r} 516 \\ -\,204 \\ \hline ? \end{array} \qquad \begin{array}{l} 516 - 4 = \;\; 512 \\ 204 - 4 = -\,200 \\ \hline \qquad\quad\;\; 312 \end{array}$$

Change the second number to a multiple of 10

1. $\begin{array}{r} 74 \\ -\,28 \\ \hline \end{array}$

2. $\begin{array}{r} 61 \\ -\,32 \\ \hline \end{array}$

3. $\begin{array}{r} 52 \\ -\,39 \\ \hline \end{array}$

4. $\begin{array}{r} 63 \\ -\,48 \\ \hline \end{array}$

5. $\begin{array}{r} 72 \\ -\,44 \\ \hline \end{array}$

6. $\begin{array}{r} 90 \\ -\,52 \\ \hline \end{array}$

7. $\begin{array}{r} 65 \\ -\,49 \\ \hline \end{array}$

8. $\begin{array}{r} 91 \\ -\,63 \\ \hline \end{array}$

9. $\begin{array}{r} 70 \\ -\,46 \\ \hline \end{array}$

10. $\begin{array}{r} 82 \\ -\,38 \\ \hline \end{array}$

11. 76 – 29 = _____
12. 53 – 49 = _____
13. 42 – 39 = _____
14. 47 – 29 = _____

Change the second number to a multiple of 100

15. $\begin{array}{r} 535 \\ -\,103 \\ \hline \end{array}$

16. $\begin{array}{r} 327 \\ -\,198 \\ \hline \end{array}$

17. $\begin{array}{r} 417 \\ -\,204 \\ \hline \end{array}$

18. $\begin{array}{r} 687 \\ -\,102 \\ \hline \end{array}$

19. $\begin{array}{r} 404 \\ -\,201 \\ \hline \end{array}$

20. $\begin{array}{r} 584 \\ -\,302 \\ \hline \end{array}$

21. $\begin{array}{r} 605 \\ -\,298 \\ \hline \end{array}$

22. $\begin{array}{r} 583 \\ -\,101 \\ \hline \end{array}$

24. $\begin{array}{r} 462 \\ -\,297 \\ \hline \end{array}$

24. $\begin{array}{r} 610 \\ -\,197 \\ \hline \end{array}$

25. 625 – 203 = _____
26. 249 – 102 = _____
27. 373 – 197 = _____
28. 484 – 103 = _____

In subtraction, either increase both numbers or decrease both numbers by the same amount.

ADDING AND SUBTRACTING MONEY

WHAT'S A WORD WORTH?

These letters of the alphabet have been given a value.

A = Rs 210.00	B = Rs 28.00	C = Rs 132.00	D = Rs 201.00	E = Rs 144.00
G = Rs 69.50	H = Rs 200.25	I = Rs 245.00	K = Rs 43.25	L = Rs 70.50
N = Rs 30.50	O = Rs 250.00	P = Rs 90.00	R = Rs 87.75	S = Rs 211.75
T = Rs 77.50	U = Rs 150.00	W = Rs 40.00	Y = Rs 93.25	

Find the value of each of these pairs of words. Then subtract them to find how much more one is worth than the other. One has been done for you.

1. DOG and CAT

D	201.00	C	132.00	DOG	520.50
O	250.00	A	210.00	CAT	– 419.50
G	+ 69.50	T	+ 77.50		Rs. 101.00
	Rs. 520.50		Rs. 419.50		

The word 'DOG' is worth more than 'CAT' by Rs 101.00.

2. PINK and BLUE

3. NOSE and NECK

4. EARTH and WATER

5. SNAIL and SNAKE

6. HOCKEY and TENNIS

7. ERASER and PENCIL

PROBLEM SOLVING

EXTRA INFORMATION

These problems have some extra information that you do not need to answer the question. Read each problem carefully and use only those facts that help you solve the problem.

1. Sheetal had a collection of 126 bookmarks. On her 10th birthday, she got 41 more bookmarks. How many bookmarks does she have now?

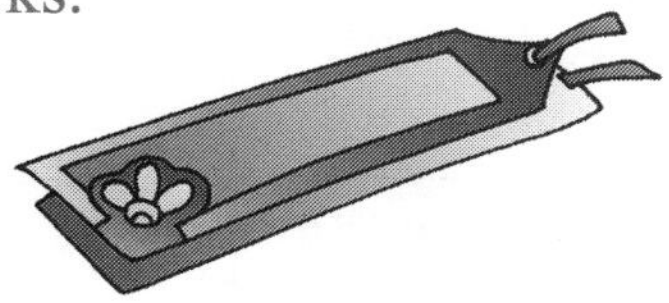

____

2. A packet of candles costs Rs 12. Each packet has 24 candles. If Manisha bought 20 packets, how many candles did she buy?

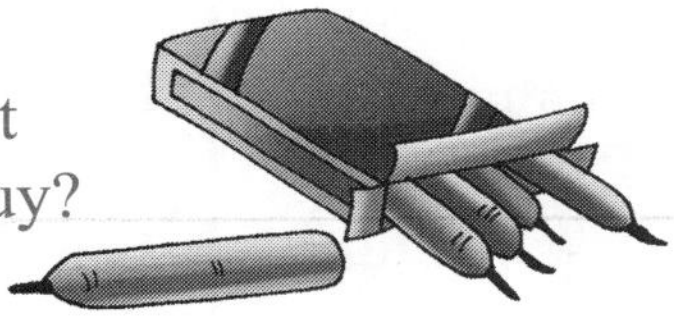

____

3. Arpita has Rs 500. She bought a book for Rs 230 and an umbrella for Rs 142. How much money did she spend?

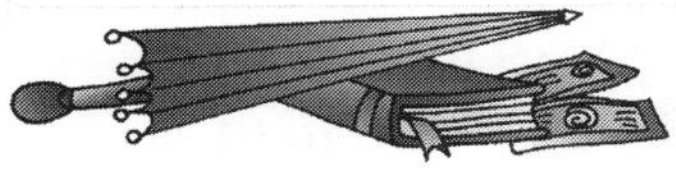

____

4. It costs Rs 850 to feed elephants at the zoo each day. The zoo has 5 elephants. How much does it cost to feed the elephants for 15 days?

____

5. 2715 people came to watch the cricket match at the stadium. 235 of them were children. There are 3000 seats at the stadium. How many seats were empty?

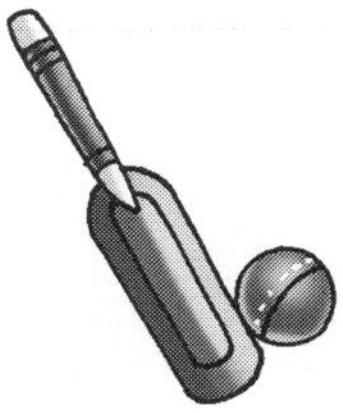

____

Fill in the cross number puzzle.

a	b		c	d
e		f		
	g			
h				i
j			k	

Clues Across

(a) 207 sweets were shared among 9 people. How many sweets did each one get?

(c) 360 students are to be divided into groups such that each group has 8 students. How many such groups can be made?

(e) There are 38976 men, 33966 women and 11234 children in a town. How many people are there in the town?

(g) There are 4554 books in 9 cartons. How many books are there in a carton?

(h) There are 612 crates with 32 bottles in each. How many bottles in all?

(j) There are 351 sheep. How many enclosures will be required if 9 sheep are kept in one enclosure?

(k) There are 216 sheets of paper. If 8 sheets are kept in a file, how many files will be required to keep all the sheets.

Clues Down

(a) 5 litres of petrol is needed per day. How many days will 140 litres of petrol last?

(b) 18562 people visited an exhibition in the morning and 16037 people visited in the evening. How many people visited the exhibition ?

(c) Tennis tournaments were played over 6 days. If 7947 people came each day, how many people came for the tournament?

(d) 336 paintings are to be packed in boxes of 6 each. How many boxes can be made?

(f) 735 books are to be placed on 7 shelves. How many books can be placed on a shelf?

(h) 78 posters were painted in 6 days. How many posters were painted in a day?

(i) There are 329 children. If there are 7 children in a team. How many teams can be made?

Teacher's tip:

For each problem that the teacher reads out, groups of students may use their arms or hands to demonstrate the symbol (+, –, × or ÷) they feel can be used to solve it.

MENTAL MATHS

1. ☐ – 100 = 145
2. Double of 80 = _________
3. Make the largest 5-digit number using 2, 3, 1, 7
4. 67 – 52 = _________
5. 3425 – 400 = _________
6. What is the value of the digit 4 in 248376?
7. 1925 + 75 = _________
8. Give the Roman Numeral for 27.
9. 3000 – 50 = _________
10. Double the sum of 10 and 15. ____
11. 65 + 19 = _________
12. Round 12875 to the nearest 1000.
13. 45 + 29 = _________
14. Give the sum of the place values of 2 in 125432. _________
15. 57 – 19 = _________
16. 130 – 89 = _________
17. 83499 is 1 less than _________
18. Write 105010 in words. _________
19. The double of a number is 28. What is its half ? _________
20. 81 ÷ ☐ = 9

21. 30000 + 200 + 5 = _________
22. Round 34527 to the nearest 100. ____
23. 40100 is 1 more than _________
24. 43 + 57 = _________
25. 34523, 35523, 36523, _________ _________ , _________
26. ☐ ÷ 5 = 9
27. 19 + ☐ = 50
28. 5634 – 34 = _________
29. Which digit is in the ten thousands place in 34254? _________
30. 2000 – 100 = _________
31. Double of Rs 2.50 = _________
32. How many 7s in 700 ? _________
33. 99 + 56 = _________
34. Find the sum of 3012 and 2300. __
35. 81 more than 119 is _________
36. 89 + 101 = _________
37. 2000 + 1111 – 1000 = _________
38. Take away 51 from 500. _______
39. Give the difference between the place values of 6 in 16564. ______
40. Add 55 to the product of 5 and 9. _________

Students may do only 10 sums at a time.

Multiplication

MULTIPLYING 4-DIGITS BY 1-DIGIT

BE A DETECTIVE!

Multiply. Then find the products in the box below and circle them. They will be in both horizontal and vertical lines. You will know you are right when you have circled all the numbers.

1. 4000 × 7 28000	2. 3400 × 6	3. 8005 × 4	4. 6020 × 8
5. 5270 × 9	6. 8401 × 5	7. 2095 × 4	8. 2269 × 5
9. 4214 × 2	10. 4583 × 2	11. 1345 × 3	12. 1096 × 8
13. 7392 × 8	14. 4539 × 6	15. 7938 × 9	16. 9673 × 7
17. 6398 × 3	18. 3419 × 4	19. 5826 × 9	

8	8	4	1	4	7	4	3	0	9
4	7	0	1	5	9	1	3	6	1
2	6	3	3	4	2	0	0	5	6
8	8	5	4	2	7	2	3	4	6
2	5	7	5	6	7	7	1	1	2
0	2	1	8	1	3	6	7	6	8
4	4	4	3	1	9	1	9	4	0
0	3	4	8	3	2	0	2	0	0
0	4	2	0	4	8	1	6	0	0

MULTIPLYING BY TENS

1. 288×20
2. 392×50
3. 723×60
4. 866×60
5. 439×30
6. 541×40
7. 654×70
8. 975×30
9. 103×80
10. 350×90
11. 500×20
12. 706×50

13. 1894×40
14. 3568×70
15. 9631×80
16. 2786×20
17. 2056×50
18. 4479×60
19. 8765×90
20. 4617×30
21. 5263×40
22. 6326×80
23. 7872×90
24. 6968×60

MULTIPLYING 3-DIGITS BY 2-DIGITS

ACTIVITY-BASED WORKSHEET

First multiply. Then help Baby Mole find his way home by shading the boxes with even products.

	1. 345 × 46	2. 488 × 59	3. 197 × 63	4. 385 × 75
5. 217 × 83	6. 275 × 97	7. 634 × 37	8. 712 × 75	9. 836 × 83
10. 583 × 83	11. 487 × 71	12. 749 × 57	13. 839 × 43	14. 973 × 68
15. 783 × 55	16 267 × 48	17. 574 × 67	18. 709 × 52	19. 814 × 82
20 877 × 59	21. 598 × 54	22. 639 × 83	23. 849 × 67	24. 625 × 39
25. 849 × 47	26. 733 × 36	27. 482 × 94	28. 830 × 69	

3-DIGIT MULTIPLICATION

1. 332×125	2. 423×778	3. 928×623
4. 640×395	5. 515×489	6. 879×106
7. 506×510	8. 217×254	9. 783×578
10. 309×435	11. 562×339	12. 664×462

MIXED PRACTICE

BESIDES WATER AND SUNLIGHT WHAT ELSE DO PLANTS USE TO MAKE OXYGEN?

Find each product. Write the letter in the box above each matching number in the decoder to get the answer.

A 396×123	**B** 543×27		
C 2364×80	**D** 593×70	**E** 8329×8	**I** 830×90
N 293×48	**O** 1846×3	**R** 931×206	**X** 7342×7

This worksheet integrates Mathematics and Science.

Decoder

___	A	___	___	___	___
189120	48708	191786	14661	5538	14064

___	___	___	___	___	___	___
41510	74700	5538	51394	74700	41510	66632

CALCULATING WITH MONEY-1

Given below are some articles and their prices in rupees and paise.

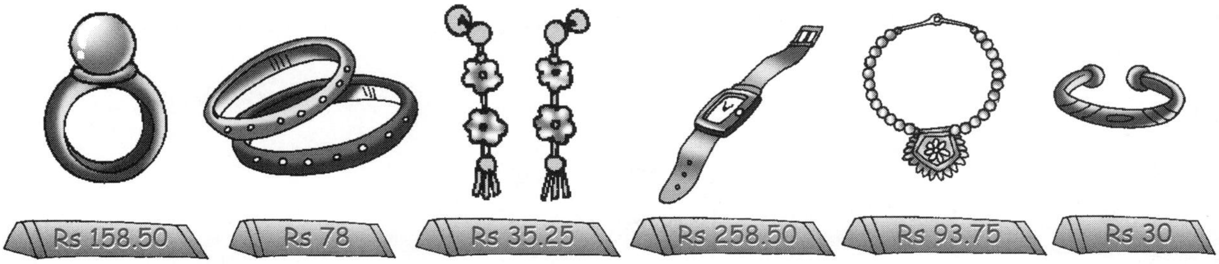

Fill in the blanks making use of the above information.

1. Shabnam bought three pairs of earrings.

   She paid Rs _________________ for them.

2. Anisha got back Rs 41.50 from Rs 300 that she gave

   at the shop. She bought a _________________ .

3. Harleen paid Rs _________________ for 5 pairs of bangles.

4. June bought two rings, two bracelets and a necklace.

   She paid Rs _________________ for them.

5. Vijaya got back Rs _________________ when she gave the

   shopkeeper Rs 500 for 3 rings.

6. The difference in price between the most expensive and

   the cheapest item is Rs _________________ .

CALCULATING WITH MONEY-2

AT THE MARKET

Mrs Singh went to the market for her weekly shopping. Here are the things she bought and the amount she paid. Match the item to the person she bought it from. One has been done for you.

(a)

1. Carrots 4 kg
   Rs 98.00

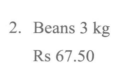

(d)

2. Beans 3 kg
   Rs 67.50

(b)

3. Potatoes 6 kg
   Rs 78.00

(e)

4. Onions 5 kg
   Rs 86.25

(c)

5. Brinjals 2 kg
   Rs 35.00

(f)

6. Tomatoes 4 kg
   Rs 86.00

PROBLEM SOLVING

PROBLEMS WITHOUT NUMBERS

The problems below do not have numbers.
Read each problem carefully and decide whether it can be solved with addition, subtraction, multiplication or division. Then circle it.

1. On Thursday ★ parents came to school for Open Day. On Friday ★ parents came to school for Open Day. How many parents attended Open Day in all?
   Add   Subtract   Multiply   Divide

2. Hiroo can put ★ photographs in ★ pages of her album. How many photographs can each page hold?
   Add   Subtract   Multiply   Divide

3. A train has ★ coaches. A coach can carry ★ people. How many passengers are there in the train?
   Add   Subtract   Multiply   Divide

4. A music shop sold ★ CDs in a particular month. Of these ★ were of classical music. How many CDs were not of classical music?
   Add   Subtract   Multiply   Divide

5. A box of paper has ★ sheets. How many sheets will be there in ★ boxes?
   Add   Subtract   Multiply   Divide

6. A recipe calls for ★ tomatoes. Mrs Kaur has ★ tomatoes. How many more does she need?
   Add   Subtract   Multiply   Divide

7. A bar of chocolate costs Rs ★. I have Rs ★ . How many bars can I buy?
   Add   Subtract   Multiply   Divide

Teacher's tip:
Cards can be placed on each of the four corners of the room showing one of each of the four operations +, –, ×, ÷. For every problem that the teacher reads out, students can go to the corner that shows the sign that they feel is needed to solve the problem.

PROBLEM SOLVING

TWO-STEP PROBLEMS

These problems will need two steps to solve them.

1. A group of 32 people who went for a picnic had two boxes of biscuits with them. One box had 82 chocolate biscuits and the other had 110 cream biscuits. If each person got the same number of biscuits, how many biscuits did each person get?

____

2. 26 children each gave Rs 15.50 for the visit to the museum. A collection of Rs 500 was needed. How much more money was required?

____

3. The students collected 75 books to add to the class library. The library already had 172 books, but 35 of these had to be given away as they were torn. How many books are there in the class library now?

____

4. 18 boxes of erasers were bought. Each box had 48 erasers. These were opened up and put into smaller packets of 6 each. How many packets could be made?

____

5. For a field trip 6 buses carried 45 children each and 3 buses carried 24 children each. How many children went for the field trip? (Hint: This may need more than two steps.)

____

MENTAL MATHS

1. $50 + 50 \times 50 =$ ______________
2. Write 102000 in words.
3. $49 \div$ ☐ $= 7$
4. 20×2 years = ______________ months
5. $1006 - 100 =$ ______________
6. $213 \times 5 = (200 \times 5) + (10 \times 5)$ + (☐ $\times 5$)
7. $90 - 19 =$ ______________
8. What is half of 70? ______________
9. $60 \times 30 =$ ______________
10. What should you multiply 29 by to make it 2900? ______________
11. $95 +$ ☐ $- 10 = 90$
12. 48635 rounded to the nearest 100 = ______________
13. $45 \times 101 =$ ______________
14. The value of 6 in 56321 = ______
15. $700 \times 20 =$ ______________
16. $30 \times$ ☐ $= 1200$
17. ☐ $- 99 = 500$
18. $23 \times 78 \times 0 =$ ______________
19. Estimated product of $51 \times 49 =$ ___
20. 5 times a number is 250. What is the number? __________
21. $50 \times 1 \times 20 =$ ______________
22. $9 \times 99 =$ ______________
23. $73 + 101 =$ ______________
24. $8 \times 13 = (8 \times$ ☐ $) + (8 \times 3)$
25. What is double of 350? ____________
26. $4 \times 29 =$ ______________
27. Estimated product of $11 \times 99 =$ ______
28. $99 + 86 =$ ______________
29. 10×4 weeks = ______________ days
30. Rs 100 – ☐ = Rs 19
31. Rs 75 + ☐ = Rs 150
32. $50 \times 19 =$ ______________
33. If $8 \times 25 = 200$, what is 16×25?
34. $101 \times 28 =$ ______________
35. ☐ $\times 40 = 200$
36. Number before 14141 is ________
37. $40 \times 300 =$ ______________
38. There are ________ paise in Rs 40.
39. Write two lakh eight in figures.

    ____
40. Give the product of 245 and 100.

    ____

Students may do only 10 sums at a time.

TEST YOUR SKILLS*

Tick (✓) the correct answer for each question.

1. What digit in the number 456238 is in the ten thousands place?
   (a) 4 (b) 5
   (c) 2 (d) 6

2. 12689 rounded off to the nearest 1000 is
   (a) 12700 (b) 13000
   (c) 12000 (d) 13689

3. Rearrange in increasing order 21284, 51248, 51482.
   (a) 21284, 51482, 51248
   (b) 21284, 51482, 51284
   (c) 51482, 51248, 21284
   (d) 21284, 51248, 51482

4. What is 10000 more than 12099?
   (a) 13099 (b) 13000
   (c) 22099 (d) 22000

5. What is 39 in Roman Numerals?
   (a) XXXIX (b) XXXXI
   (c) XXXI (d) XXIX

6. $\begin{array}{r} 49675 \\ +58465 \\ \hline \end{array}$
   (a) 108130 (b) 107140
   (c) 181400 (d) 108140

7. $\begin{array}{r} 70002 \\ -53956 \\ \hline \end{array}$
   (a) 16046 (b) 16846
   (c) 17648 (d) 16844

8. $\begin{array}{r} 567 \\ \times 409 \\ \hline \end{array}$
   (a) 201903 (b) 231903
   (c) 241903 (d) 231913

9. Rs 45 + Rs 17.25 – Rs 23.50 = ?
   (a) Rs 28.75 (b) Rs 38.25
   (c) Rs 38.50 (d) Rs 38.75

10. How much change will you get back from a Rs 100 note if you buy five notebooks each costing Rs 17.50?
    (a) Rs 12.50 (b) Rs 22.50
    (c) Rs 82.50 (d) Rs 87.50

11. There are 2345 trees in the orchard. Of these, 1345 are giving fruits. How many are not giving fruits?
    (a) 3969 (b) 3699
    (c) 1000 (d) 1991

12. 12345 people live in a residential colony. The next colony has 3498 more people than that. How many people are there in the next colony?
    (a) 15842 (b) 15843
    (c) 8843 (d) 8847

*This is for chapters 1,2,3.

Division

DIVIDING 4-DIGIT NUMBERS

4-DIGIT QUOTIENTS WITHOUT REMAINDER

1. $2\overline{)2482}$
2. $3\overline{)3849}$
3. $4\overline{)8624}$
4. $5\overline{)8555}$
5. $6\overline{)6648}$
6. $7\overline{)8134}$
7. $8\overline{)9688}$
8. $9\overline{)9999}$

4-DIGIT QUOTIENTS WITH REMAINDER

9. $2\overline{)3587}$
10. $3\overline{)3734}$
11. $4\overline{)8861}$
12. $5\overline{)7578}$
13. $6\overline{)6841}$
14. $7\overline{)9238}$
15. $8\overline{)8914}$
16. $9\overline{)9920}$

ZEROES IN THE QUOTIENT

Divide. Find each remainder in the boxes below and shade to find a picture.

3 ⟌ 2117	4 ⟌ 3227	9 ⟌ 1875	6 ⟌ 3059
8 ⟌ 2450	7 ⟌ 4976	5 ⟌ 4542	4 ⟌ 3638
5 ⟌ 2048	6 ⟌ 4257	8 ⟌ 4860	5 ⟌ 4049

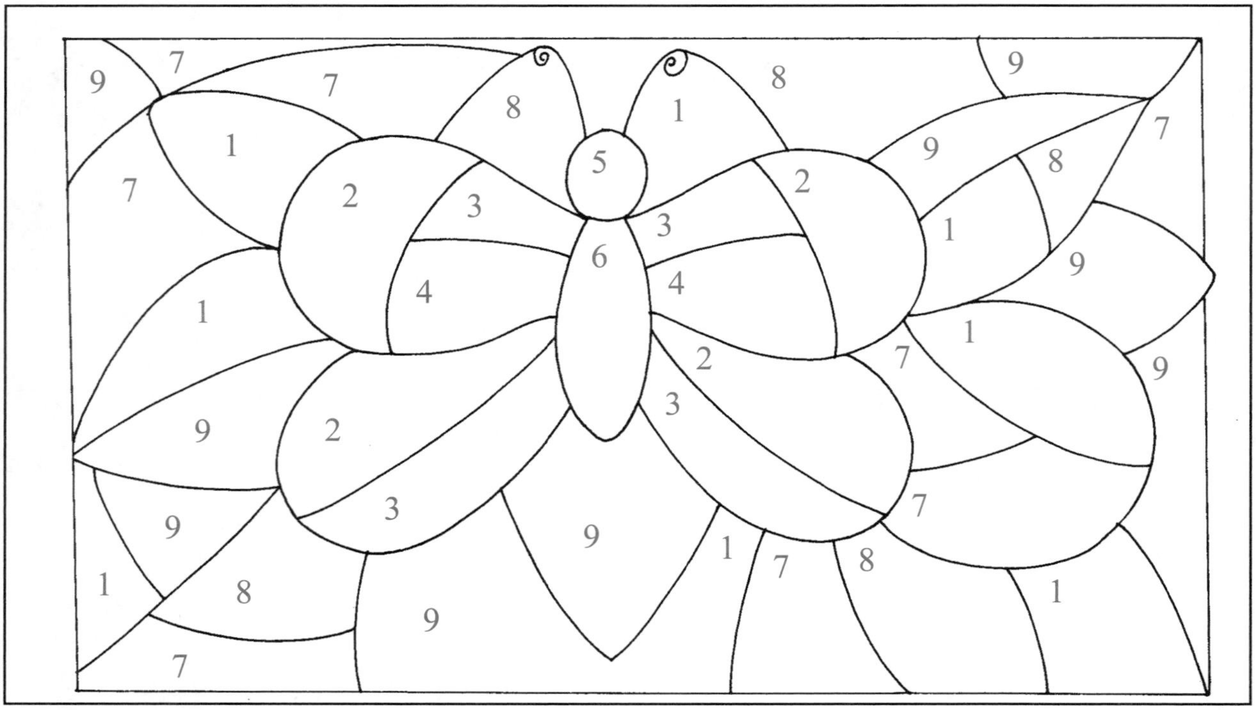

DIVIDING BY TENS

WHICH STONES DID MAMMA KANGAROO HOP ON TO REACH BABY JOEY?

Divide. Then join the stones with remainder starting from 1 going to 10.

1. 30) 281
2. 30) 975
3. 40) 293

4. 30) 301
5. 20) 302
   Quotient: 15
   − 20
   102
   − 100
   2
6. 10) 163
7. 40) 364
8. 60) 975
9. 20) 512
10. 70) 847
11. 60) 906
12. 50) 755
13. 30) 765
14. 80) 648
15. 90) 819
16. 40) 290

2-DIGIT DIVISORS

PRACTICE WORKSHEET

Workout the following division sums. One has been done for you.

1. 24 ⟌ 768 = 32
   - 768
   - − 72
   - 48
   - − 48
   - 00

2. 98 ⟌ 196

3. 61 ⟌ 549

4. 37 ⟌ 819

5. 62 ⟌ 808

6. 83 ⟌ 249

7. 19 ⟌ 398

8. 73 ⟌ 514

9. 75 ⟌ 458

10. 29 ⟌ 232

11. 23 ⟌ 329

12. 21 ⟌ 651

13. 57 ⟌ 855

SELF-CORRECTING WORKSHEET

MIXED PRACTICE

WHAT WAS THE VALUE OF THE INDIAN RUPEE IN THE SMALLEST UNIT AT THE TIME OF INDEPENDENCE?

Find each quotient. Cross out the box below that gives the quotient. You may ignore the remainders. The boxes that are not crossed out will give you the answer.

1 rupee = 16 annas
1 anna = 4 pice
1 pice = 3 pies

24 ⟌ 96 (quotient 4; − 96; 00)	16 ⟌ 95	3 ⟌ 2358	5 ⟌ 1039
80 ⟌ 800	60 ⟌ 452	17 ⟌ 442	25 ⟌ 475
31 ⟌ 175	66 ⟌ 670	75 ⟌ 908	83 ⟌ 269

Q 7	Q 701	Q 4	Q 75	Q 83	Q 10	Q 12	Q 26	Q 207
7	1	8	9	2	0	6	8	4

1 ___ ___ ___

Q 10	Q 5	Q 95	Q 5	Q 77	Q 19	Q 15	Q 786	Q 28	Q 3
a	c	p	d	i	m	e	o	s	t

p ___ ___ ___ ___

PROBLEM SOLVING WITH DIVISION

IT'S A PICNIC!

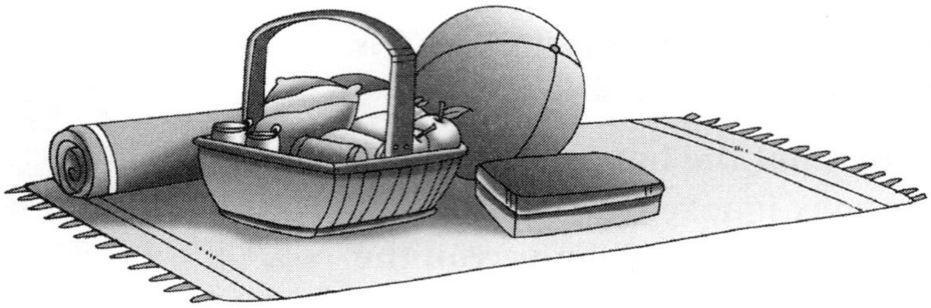

Be careful as to what the quotient and remainder mean in these division sums.

1. A carton of juice can fill 8 glasses. How many cartons will be needed to be bought if there are 135 children at the picnic?

____

2. 82 students want to play in teams. How many teams can be made if there are 9 children in a team?

____

3. The photographs of the picnic cost Rs 12 each. How many pictures can be bought with Rs 100?

____

4. The school sent one supervisor to look after groups of 20 children. How many supervisors were needed for 135 children?

____

5. Sheela had Rs 125 to spend at the picnic. She bought ice creams costing Rs 17 each for her friends. How many ice creams did she buy? How much money did she have left with her?

____

6. Each table can hold 15 people. How many tables will be needed for 135 children and 10 adults?

____

PRACTICE WORKSHEET

PROBLEM SOLVING

CHOOSE THE QUESTION

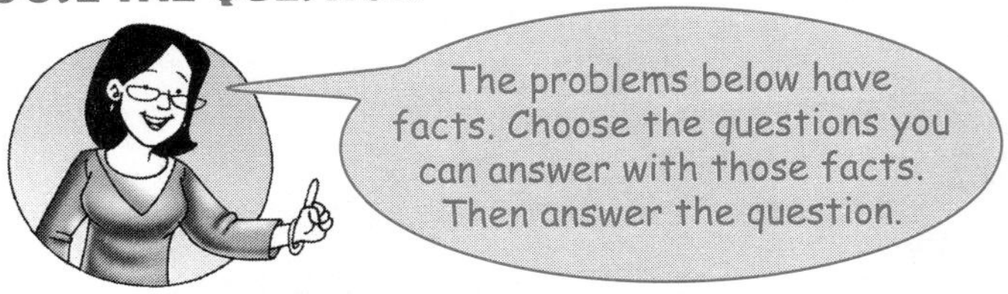

The problems below have facts. Choose the questions you can answer with those facts. Then answer the question.

1. 275 people attended the music concert. Of these, 124 were men.
   (a) How many musicians played at the concert?
   (b) How many women attended the concert?
   (c) How many people came early?

2. A restaurant served 367 people for lunch and 452 people for dinner.
   (a) How many people ate at the restaurant that day?
   (b) How many people who came to the restaurant were children?
   (c) How many people ordered ice cream for dessert?

3. The gardener bought 125 bags of saplings to plant. There were 50 saplings in a bag.
   (a) How many more saplings did he buy this year than last year?
   (b) How much did the saplings cost him?
   (c) How many saplings did he plant in the garden?

4. The Singh family went on a driving holiday. They drove 1557 km in 9 days.
   (a) How far was it from their house to their first stop?
   (b) How much did they drive each day if they travelled the same distance daily?
   (c) How much did Mr Singh drive and how much did Mrs Singh drive?

5. A boatman charges Rs 145 to go from one bank of the river to the other. He had 56 passengers on Monday.
   (a) How much money did he make on Monday?
   (b) How much more money did he make on Sunday than on Monday?
   (c) How many people did he take on his boat through the week?

Teacher's tip:
A group oral assessment may be done by the teacher calling each question above, and the students showing a 'thumbs up' signal if they think the question can be answered and 'thumbs down' signal if they feel it cannot be answered.

MULTIPLYING AND DIVIDING WITH MONEY

Mrs Rao bought art material for her children. This is the bill she paid.

PICASSO ART STORE

Number of Items	Item	Amount Rs. p
9 bottles	Poster colours	256.50
7	Brushes	85.75
2	Pallettes	30.00
5 boxes	Crayons	59.75
2	Drawing books	27.00
	Total	**459.00**

1. Use the bill to fill in the answers below:

(a) Cost of 1 brush Rs ______________ .

(b) Cost of 1 box of crayons Rs ______________ .

(c) Cost of 1 bottle of poster colours Rs ______________ .

(d) Cost of 1 pallette Rs ______________ .

(e) Cost of 1 drawing book Rs ______________ .

2. Now use the above to answer these:

(a) Cost of 3 brushes Rs ______________ .

(b) Cost of 9 drawing books Rs ______________ .

(c) Cost of 5 bottles of poster colours Rs ______________ .

(d) Cost of 2 boxes of crayons Rs ______________ .

(e) Cost of 6 pallettes Rs ______________ .

PROBLEM SOLVING

SETTING UP A HOUSE!

1. A dining table costs Rs 2341. A set of chairs costs Rs 3987. How much would you have to pay for both?

   ____

2. A brand new sofa set costs Rs 9600. A second hand sofa set costs Rs 5432. How much do you save by buying a second hand sofa set?

   ____

3. Bathroom tiles cost Rs 235 for a box. If you need 45 boxes to tile your bathrooms, how much money do you need?

   ____

4. There are 4 rooms in the house. If you have to put a wall clock costing Rs 309 in each room, how much money will you spend?

   ____

5. It costs Rs 3580 to put curtains in 4 rooms. How much will it cost if curtains are put only in one room?

   ____

6. A new refrigerator costs Rs 9540. How much will you pay per month if the shopkeeper lets you pay the money in equal amounts over 12 months?

   ____

7. A set of bed covers cost Rs 1980. A set of mattresses costs Rs 1432 more than that. How much does a set of mattresses cost?

   ____

HIGHER ORDER THINKING SKILLS

1. 

There are 346 coins in the piggy bank. There are the same number of 5-rupee coins and 2-rupee coins. How much money is in the piggy bank?

2. You have Rs 100. Toffees cost Rs 5 each and chocolates are 3 for Rs 20. If you spent the entire amount, what exactly did you buy if you bought 17 items in all?

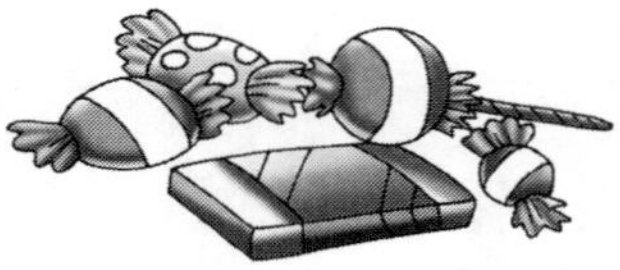

3. 

Anjaney bought a magnetic sticker for Rs 25. He sold it to a friend for Rs 29. Later he bought it back from the friend for Rs 36 and sold it to another friend for Rs 37. How much did he make or lose in the end?

4. A pile of 10 five-rupee coins is about 2 cm high. How much money is there in a pile that is 20 cm high?

5. 

A bag of coins is worth 18 rupees. It has a combination of 5-rupee, 2-rupee and 1-rupee coins. What is the least number of coins of each denomination that it can contain?

MENTAL MATHS

1. 450 ÷ 90 = ________
2. How many pairs in 27 shoes? ________
3. Double of 49 = ________
4. How many rolls of 2 m ribbons should I buy if I need 11 m of ribbons?
5. If I drive 84 km in a week, how much do I drive in a day? ________
6. Write the smallest 6-digit numeral.
7. 765 ÷ 10 = Q _____ , R _____
8. How many 5s in 40? ________
9. There are _____ hundreds in 3400.
10. Half of 250 = ________
11. What is the sum of all the numbers on a dice? ________
12. ☐ ÷ 10 = 52
13. 200 ÷ 40 = ________
14. If 30 eggs can be put in one egg tray, how many eggs can be put in $2\frac{1}{2}$ trays? ________
15. What is my change from Rs 25 if I spend Rs 12.50? ________
16. 300 ÷ 60 = ________
17. The number after 989999 is ________
18. 120 flowers = ________ dozens
19. How many 7s in 91? ________
20. 140 ÷ 7 ☐ 3 × 7 (use >, < or =)
21. 400 wheels can be put on how many cars?
22. What is1000 more than 4976?
23. What is the price of one if 100 costs Rs 5000? ________
24. How many bangle stands are needed for 16 bangles if each stand holds 6 bangles?
25. How many 7s in 63? ________
26. 5700 ÷ ☐ = 57
27. What is the product of 7, 5, and 2?
28. Write the largest 5-digit number.
29. Half of 98 = ________
30. 1498 ÷ 100 = Q ______, R _______
31. ☐ ÷ 5 = 12
32. If 15 × 4 = 60, what is 15 × 8?
33. 4 pastries cost Rs 56. How much does one cost? ________
34. How many packets needed for 200 sweets, if each packet holds 50 sweets? ________
35. Double of 56 = ________
36. How many times 20 is 2000? ______
37. Half of 74 = ________
38. 720 ÷ 80 = ________
39. The number before 437650 = ______
40. Write 3400 paise in rupees. _______

Students may do only 10 sums at a time.

Factors and Multiples

5

FACTORS

1. List the factors of these numbers:

(a) 12 1 2 3 4 6 12

(b) 16 ______

(c) 18 ______

(d) 24 ______

(e) 28 ______

(f) 30 ______

(g) 32 ______

(h) 35 ______

2. Use the factors above to fill in the circles. Write the common factors on the shaded part.

(a)

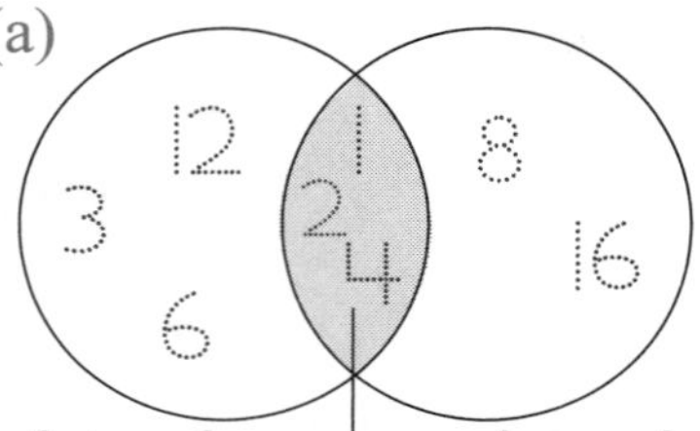

factors of 12 | common factors of 12 and 16 | factors of 16

(b)

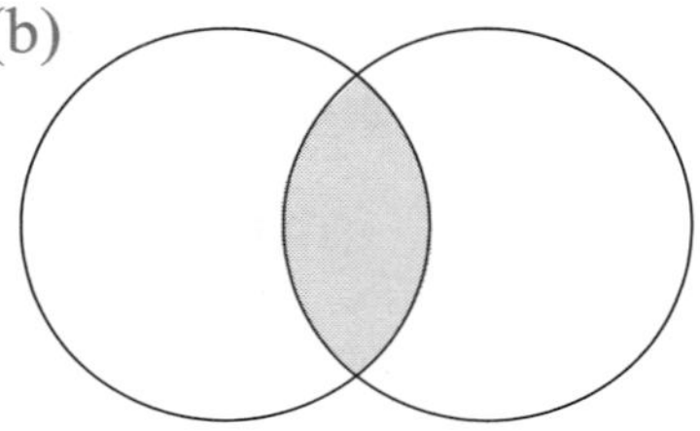

12 18

(c)

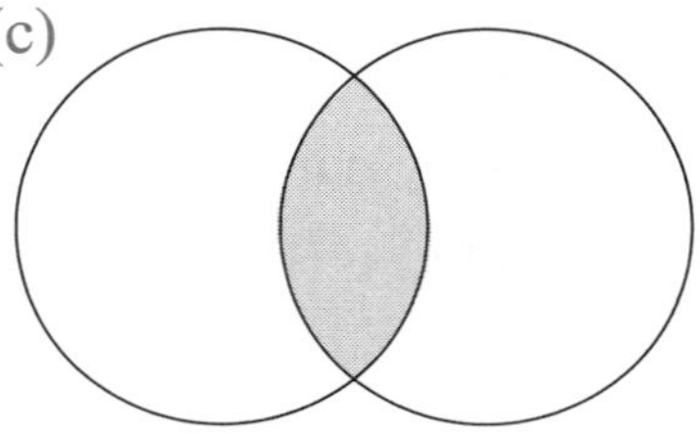

16 18

(d)

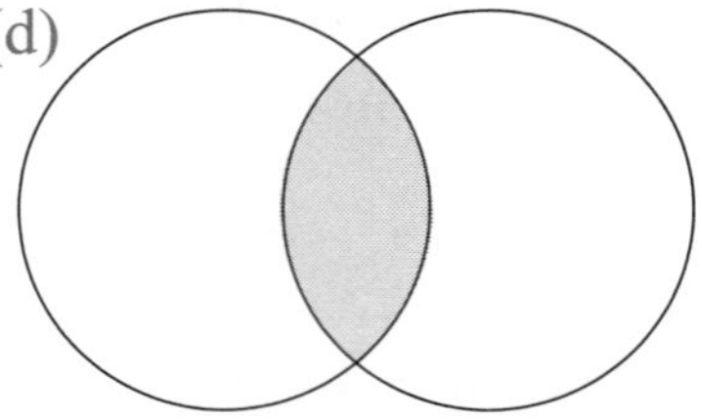

18 24

(e)

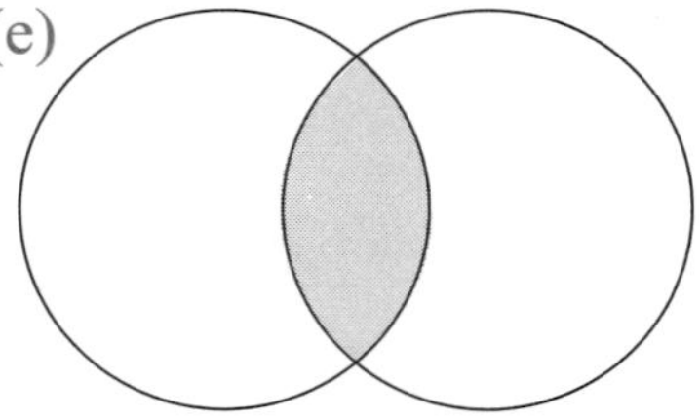

24 28

(f)

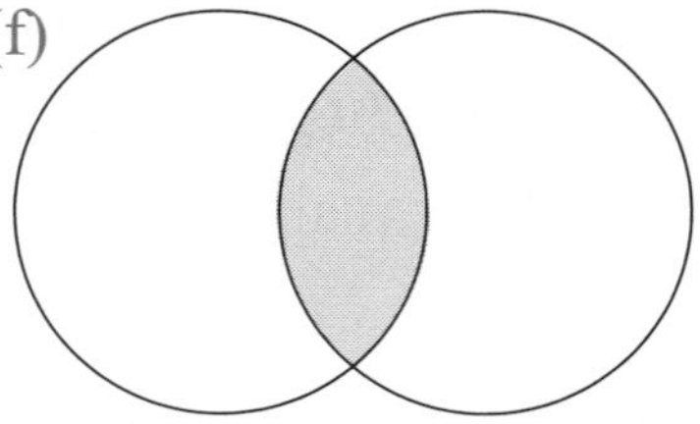

18 28

(g)

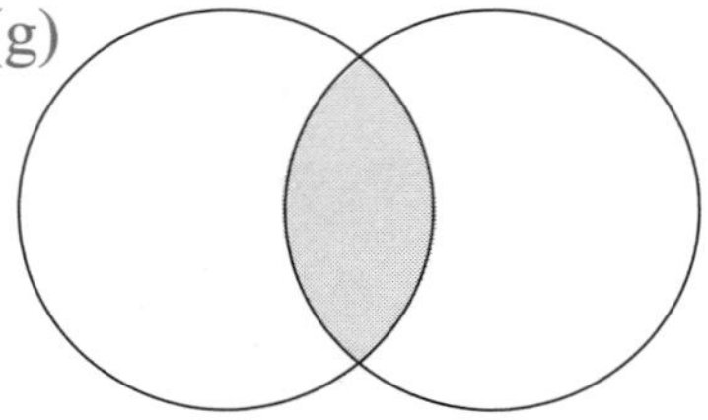

28 30

(h)

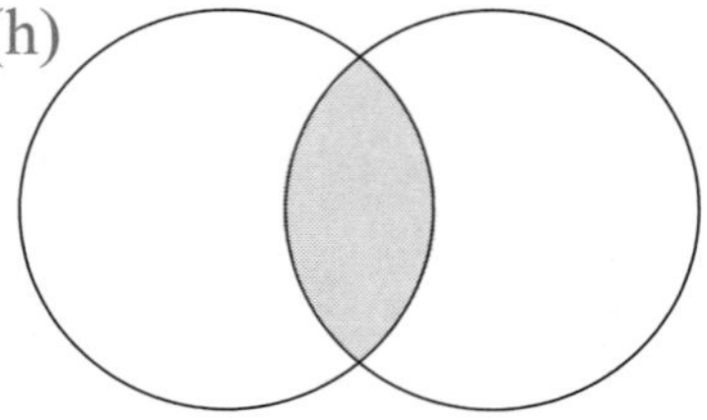

30 32

(i)

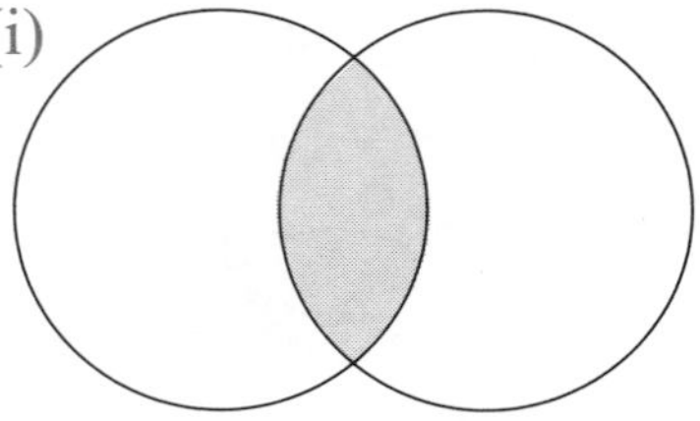

30 35

FACTORISATION

Factor Trees

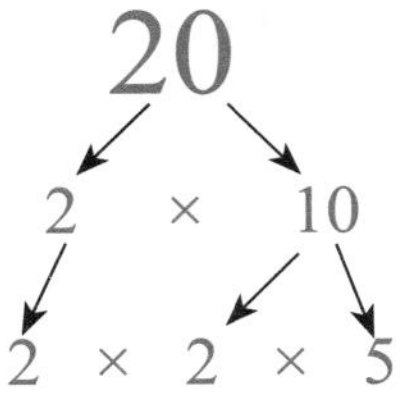

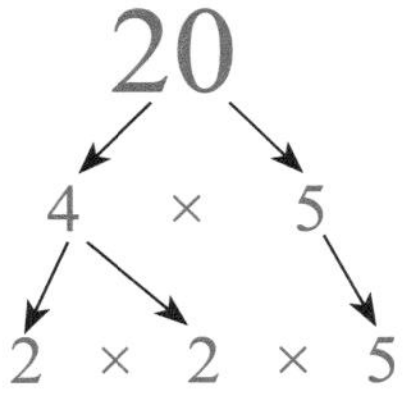

16 16 18 18

12 12 28 28

24 24 24

36 36 36

40 40 40

42 42 42

MULTIPLES

1. **Give the first 10 multiples of each.**

(a) 3 3 6 ______ ______ ______ ______ ______ ______ ______ ______

(b) 4 ______ ______ ______ ______ ______ ______ ______ ______ ______ ______

(c) 6 ______ ______ ______ ______ ______ ______ ______ ______ ______ ______

(d) 5 ______ ______ ______ ______ ______ ______ ______ ______ ______ ______

(e) 8 ______ ______ ______ ______ ______ ______ ______ ______ ______ ______

(f) 9 ______ ______ ______ ______ ______ ______ ______ ______ ______ ______

(g) 10 ______ ______ ______ ______ ______ ______ ______ ______ ______ ______

2. **Use the answers above to list the common multiples of these numbers.**

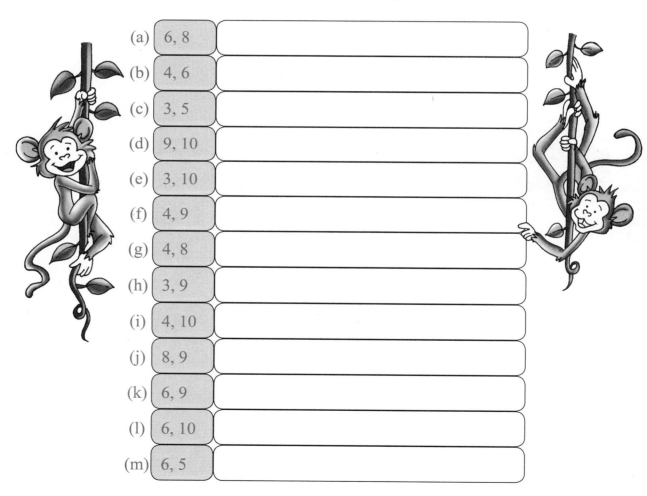

(a)	6, 8	
(b)	4, 6	
(c)	3, 5	
(d)	9, 10	
(e)	3, 10	
(f)	4, 9	
(g)	4, 8	
(h)	3, 9	
(i)	4, 10	
(j)	8, 9	
(k)	6, 9	
(l)	6, 10	
(m)	6, 5	

COMMON MULTIPLES

ACTIVITY-BASED WORKSHEET

Repeat the names shown. Then shade the boxes that have the last letter of each name. The shaded boxes will show you the common multiples.

1.

1 J	2 O	3 J	4 O	5 J	6 O	7 J	8 O	9 J	10 O	11 J	12 O	13 J	14 O	15 J	16 O	17 J	18 O	19 J	20 O
1 A	2 L	3 O	4 K	5 A	6 L	7 O	8 K	9 A	10 L	11 O	12 K	13 A	14 L	15 O	16 K	17 A	18 L	19 O	20 K

JO – 2 letters ALOK – 4 letters

Common multiples of 2 and 4 are 4, 8, 4, 8, ____________

2.

1 R	2 I	3 T	4 A	5 R	6 I	7 T	8	9	10	11	12	13	14	15	16	17	18	19	20
1 P	2 R	3 I	4 T	5 A	6 M	7 P	8 R	9	10	11	12	13	14	15	16	17	18	19	20

RITA – 4 letters PRITAM – 6 letters

Common multiples of 4 and 6 are ____________

3.

1 D	2 E	3 V	4	5	6	7	8	9	10	11	12	13	14	15	16	17	18	19	20
1 R	2 A	3 H	4 U	5 L	6	7	8	9	10	11	12	13	14	15	16	17	18	19	20

DEV – 3 letters RAHUL – 5 letters

Common multiples of 3 and 5 are ____________

4.

1 R	2 O	3 S	4 H	5 A	6 N	7	8	9	10	11	12	13	14	15	16	17	18	19	20
1 A	2 L	3 I	4	5	6	7	8	9	10	11	12	13	14	15	16	17	18	19	20

ROSHAN – ____________ letters ALI – ____________ letters

Common multiples of 3 and 6 are ____________

HIGHER ORDER THINKING SKILLS

1. Shade the factors of 60 that lie next to each other. There are 10 sets.

7	6	2	5	9	11	4	15	8	6	10	8	4	3	5	7	5
																12
	3	7	2	2	15	13	9	2	30	11	8	7	3	20	7	9
	2															
	10	9	2	2	3	5	8	7								

2. A plane takes off for a domestic destination every 5 minutes, and every 9 minutes for an international destination. The last time both planes took off at the same time was at 7 a.m. At what time will that happen next?

____

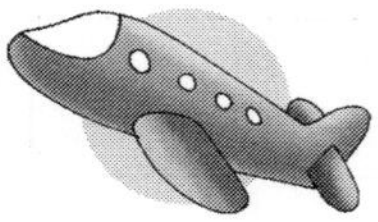

3. Who am I?
   (a) I am more than 62. I am not a multiple of 2, 3 or 5. I am less than 71. Who am I?

   (b) I am an even multiple of 7. If you reverse my digits, I become a multiple of 8.

4.

 +  = Rs 15

 –  = Rs 3

 = ?

 = ?

QUIZ !

1. Name the smallest factor. ______________
2. The multiples of a number are equal to or less than a number. True or false?
3. Besides 1 and 49 which is the other factor of 49? ______________
4. Name the first five multiples of 100. ______________
5. 1, 4, 8, 12, 16 are all multiples of 4. True or false? ______________
6. Can an odd number (other than 1) be a factor of an even number? _________
7. What is the least number of factors a number can have? ______________
8. What is the factor of every number? ______________
9. 19 is one factor of 57. What is the other? (do not include 1) ____________
10. Is 37 a multiple of 7? ______________

11. The factors of 34 are 3 and 4. True of false? ______________
12. Can an even number be a factor of an odd number? ______________
13. What is the common factor of 3 and 5? ______________
14. 1 is a multiple of every number. True or false? ______________
15. Give the first two common multiples of 4 and 5. ______________
16. Since $6 \times 7 = 42$, 42 is a multiple of both 6 and 7. True or false? ______
17. Which are the common factors of 21 and 27? ______________
18. The factors of a number are equal to or less than the number. True or false? ______________
19. Circle the factors of 25— 1, 2, 5, 20, 25
20. Circle the multiples of 7— 14, 49, 54, 82

Fractions

6

EQUIVALENT FRACTIONS

Give two equivalent fractions for each picture. One has been done for you.

1. 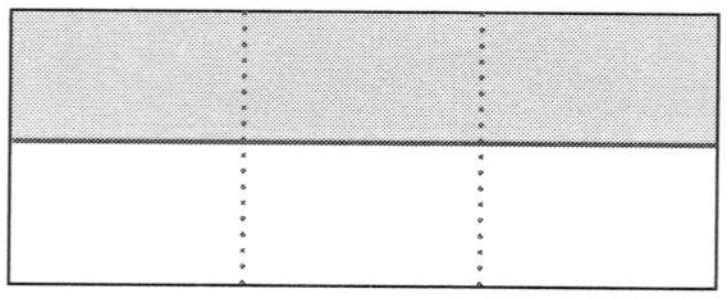

$\frac{1}{2}$ $\frac{3}{6}$

2. 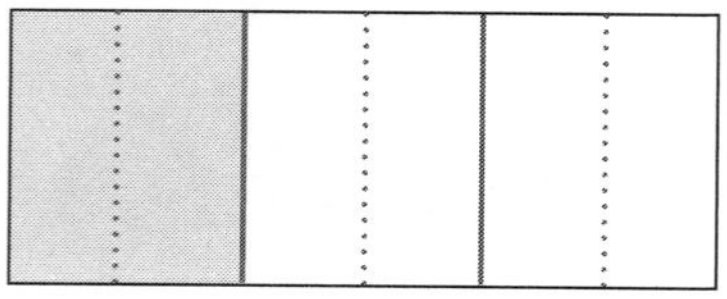

____ ____

3. 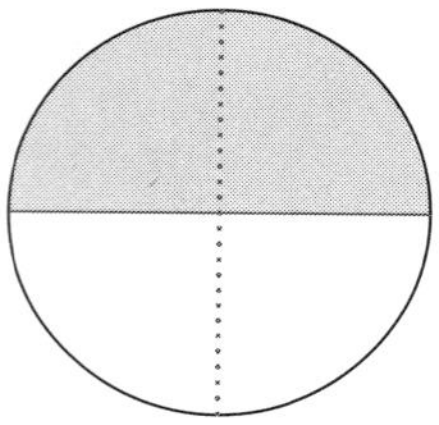

____ ____

4. 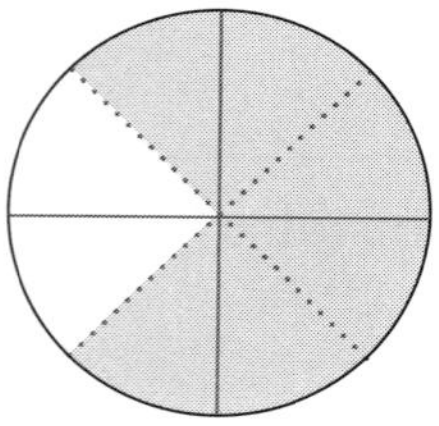

____ ____

5. 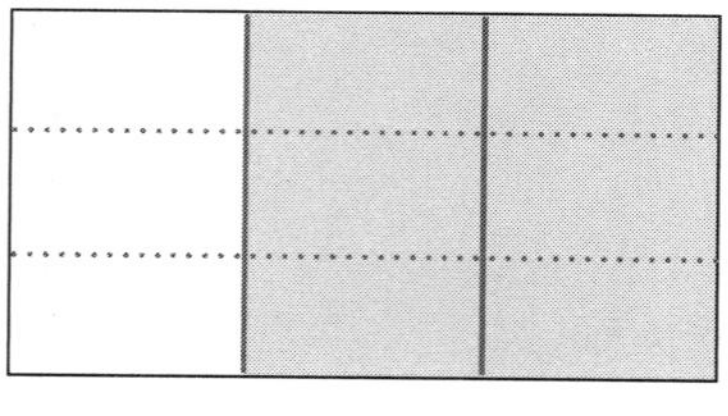

____ ____

6. 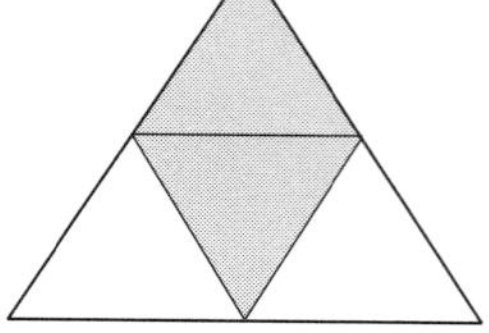

____ ____

7. 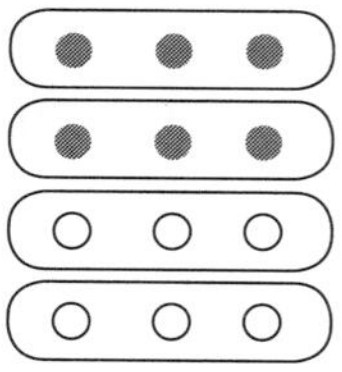

____ ____

8. 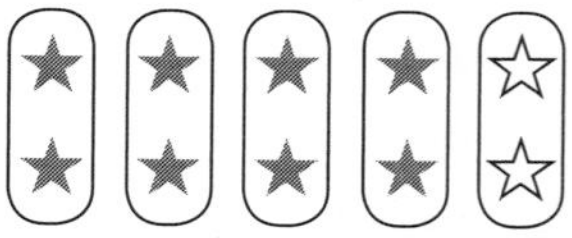

____ ____

9. 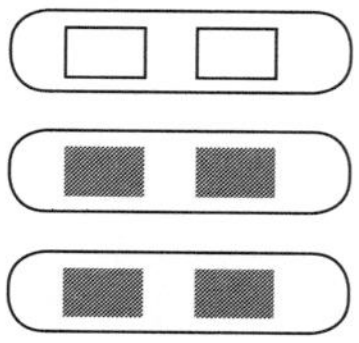

____ ____

10. 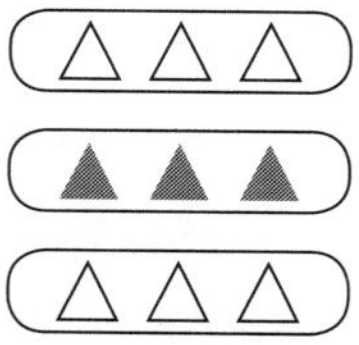

____ ____

11. 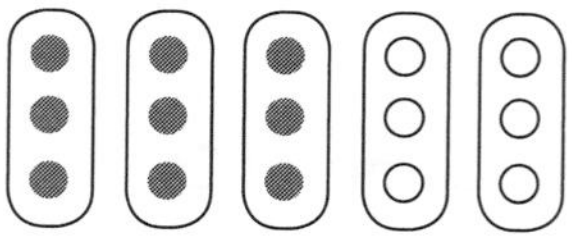

____ ____

12. 

____ ____

COMPARING LIKE FRACTIONS

Compare the following fractions. Use < or >. One has been done for you.

1. $\frac{3}{9}$ (>) $\frac{1}{9}$
2. $\frac{7}{11}$ ◯ $\frac{5}{11}$
3. $\frac{7}{8}$ ◯ $\frac{6}{8}$
4. $\frac{6}{5}$ ◯ $\frac{4}{5}$
5. $\frac{9}{13}$ ◯ $\frac{10}{13}$
6. $\frac{3}{9}$ ◯ $\frac{5}{9}$
7. $\frac{5}{7}$ ◯ $\frac{9}{7}$
8. $\frac{3}{6}$ ◯ $\frac{2}{6}$
9. $\frac{3}{4}$ ◯ $\frac{1}{4}$
10. $\frac{2}{3}$ ◯ $\frac{1}{3}$
11. $\frac{4}{5}$ ◯ $\frac{3}{5}$
12. $\frac{5}{8}$ ◯ $\frac{7}{8}$
13. $\frac{1}{7}$ ◯ $\frac{2}{7}$
14. $\frac{11}{17}$ ◯ $\frac{13}{17}$
15. $\frac{9}{21}$ ◯ $\frac{7}{21}$
16. $\frac{5}{12}$ ◯ $\frac{2}{12}$
17. $\frac{4}{5}$ ◯ $\frac{3}{5}$
18. $\frac{13}{16}$ ◯ $\frac{9}{16}$

Check your answers!

Help Froggy catch the fly. Place a counter on the frog and move it to show his jumps. Start from sum 1. End at sum 18.

(>) means move one leaf ahead.

(<) means move one leaf back.

You will know your answers are right if Froggy reaches the last leaf and catches the fly on sum 18.

ADDING LIKE FRACTIONS

Add across. Add down.
You will know you are right when the fraction in the circled corner is equal to 1.

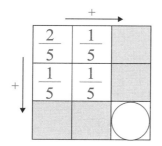

$\frac{2}{5}$	$\frac{1}{5}$	
$\frac{1}{5}$	$\frac{1}{5}$	
		○

$\frac{2}{5}$	$\frac{1}{5}$	$\frac{3}{5}$
$\frac{1}{5}$	$\frac{1}{5}$	$\frac{2}{5}$
		○

$\frac{2}{5}$	$\frac{1}{5}$	$\frac{3}{5}$
$\frac{1}{5}$	$\frac{1}{5}$	$\frac{2}{5}$
$\frac{3}{5}$	$\frac{2}{5}$	○

$\frac{2}{5}$	$\frac{1}{5}$	$\frac{3}{5}$
$\frac{1}{5}$	$\frac{1}{5}$	$\frac{2}{5}$
$\frac{3}{5}$	$\frac{2}{5}$	$\frac{5}{5}$

$\frac{2}{7}$	$\frac{3}{7}$	
$\frac{1}{7}$	$\frac{1}{7}$	
		○

$\frac{2}{11}$	$\frac{4}{11}$	
$\frac{2}{11}$	$\frac{3}{11}$	
		○

$\frac{3}{9}$	$\frac{3}{9}$	
$\frac{2}{9}$	$\frac{1}{9}$	
		○

$\frac{5}{13}$	$\frac{4}{13}$	
$\frac{1}{13}$	$\frac{3}{13}$	
		○

$\frac{4}{10}$	$\frac{3}{10}$	
$\frac{2}{10}$	$\frac{1}{10}$	
		○

$\frac{2}{8}$	$\frac{4}{8}$	
$\frac{1}{8}$	$\frac{1}{8}$	
		○

PRACTICE WORKSHEET

SUBTRACTING LIKE FRACTIONS

Subtract the fraction in the middle ring from the fraction in the inner circle. Write the difference in the outer ring.

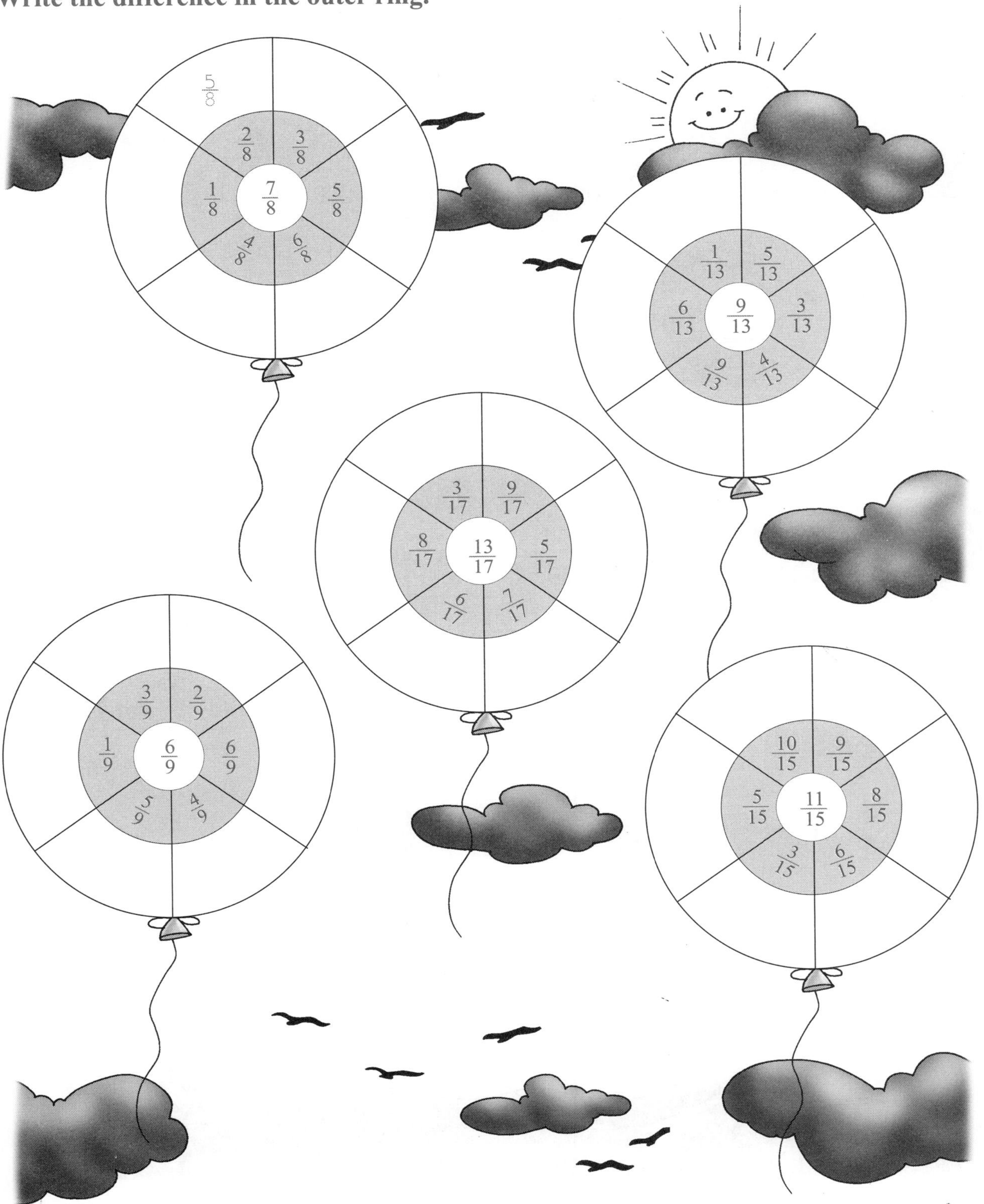

FINDING THE FRACTION OF A NUMBER

SELF-CORRECTING WORKSHEET

Find the number. You will know you are right when you see a pattern in each row of answers.

1. (a) $\frac{1}{2}$ of 4 = $\square$ (b) $\frac{2}{6}$ of 12 = $\square$ (c) $\frac{3}{4}$ of 8 = $\square$ (d) $\frac{1}{4}$ of 32 = $\square$

2. (a) $\frac{2}{3}$ of 15 = $\square$ (b) $\frac{3}{4}$ of 12 = $\square$ (c) $\frac{2}{5}$ of 20 = $\square$ (d) $\frac{1}{3}$ of 21 = $\square$

3. (a) $\frac{2}{3}$ of 18 = $\square$ (b) $\frac{13}{15}$ of 15 = $\square$ (c) $\frac{7}{8}$ of 16 = $\square$ (d) $\frac{5}{7}$ of 21 = $\square$

4. (a) $\frac{2}{5}$ of 25 = $\square$ (b) $\frac{5}{7}$ of 28 = $\square$ (c) $\frac{5}{8}$ of 48 = $\square$ (d) $\frac{8}{9}$ of 45 = $\square$

5. (a) $\frac{5}{8}$ of 16 = $\square$ (b) $\frac{3}{4}$ of 20 = $\square$ (c) $\frac{2}{7}$ of 70 = $\square$ (d) $\frac{5}{7}$ of 35 = $\square$

6. (a) $\frac{2}{7}$ of 42 = $\square$ (b) $\frac{1}{5}$ of 45 = $\square$ (c) $\frac{2}{9}$ of 27 = $\square$ (d) $\frac{1}{8}$ of 24 = $\square$

7. (a) $\frac{2}{5}$ of 10 = $\square$ (b) $\frac{4}{7}$ of 14 = $\square$ (c) $\frac{4}{6}$ of 24 = $\square$ (d) $\frac{8}{9}$ of 36 = $\square$

8. (a) $\frac{4}{5}$ of 50 = $\square$ (b) $\frac{5}{8}$ of 32 = $\square$ (c) $\frac{2}{11}$ of 55 = $\square$ (d) $\frac{1}{10}$ of 50 = $\square$

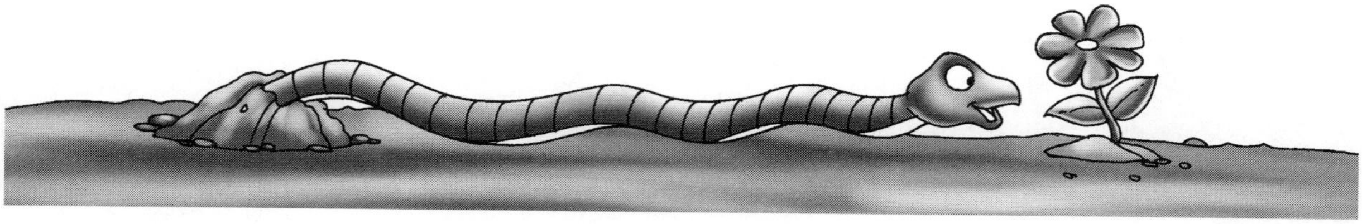

CONVERTING IMPROPER FRACTIONS AND MIXED NUMBERS

1. Change to mixed or whole number. Then join the dots in the order of the answers.

(a) $\frac{21}{6} = 3\frac{3}{6}$	(b) $\frac{23}{7} = 3\frac{2}{7}$	(c) $\frac{26}{6}$	(d) $\frac{19}{8}$
(e) $\frac{18}{6}$	(f) $\frac{11}{7}$	(g) $\frac{11}{4}$	(h) $\frac{10}{8}$
(i) $\frac{14}{7}$	(j) $\frac{16}{3}$	(k) $\frac{26}{8}$	(l) $\frac{26}{3}$
(m) $\frac{36}{8}$	(n) $\frac{25}{6}$	(o) $\frac{24}{9}$	(p) $\frac{12}{5}$
(q) $\frac{15}{10}$	(r) $\frac{32}{6}$	(s) $\frac{49}{7}$	(t) $\frac{18}{4}$

2. Change to an improper fraction. Then join the dots in the order of the answers.

(a) $1\frac{2}{3}$	(b) $2\frac{1}{4}$	(c) $1\frac{5}{8}$	(d) $2\frac{1}{3}$
(e) $4\frac{1}{5}$	(f) $3\frac{1}{2}$	(g) $2\frac{3}{5}$	(h) $1\frac{2}{5}$
(i) $3\frac{3}{8}$	(j) $4\frac{3}{7}$	(k) $3\frac{2}{7}$	(l) $3\frac{3}{9}$
(m) $1\frac{2}{9}$	(n) $5\frac{6}{7}$	(o) $1\frac{3}{8}$	(p) $4\frac{3}{5}$
(q) $2\frac{3}{7}$	(r) $1\frac{1}{3}$	(s) $5\frac{3}{5}$	(t) $2\frac{2}{9}$

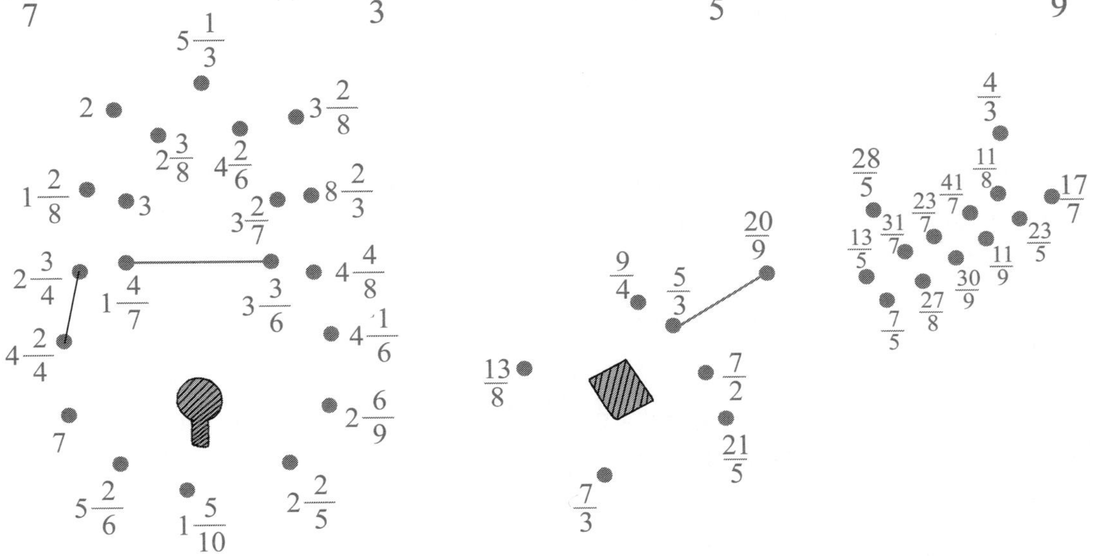

PROBLEM SOLVING

1. 

Our weight on the moon is $\frac{1}{6}$th of our weight on earth. If Shabnam weighs 54 kg on earth, how much will she weigh on the moon?

____

2. The first spacewalk was done in March 1965 by Russian astronaut Alexei Leonov. He walked in space for about $\frac{1}{5}$th of an hour. How many minutes was that?

____

3. 

About $\frac{3}{5}$th of our body weight is made up of water. What is the water content in the body of a person who weighs 70 kg?

____

4. Air is made up of many gases. About $\frac{4}{5}$th is made up of nitrogen and about $\frac{1}{5}$th is made up of oxygen. About how much more nitrogen is there than oxygen?

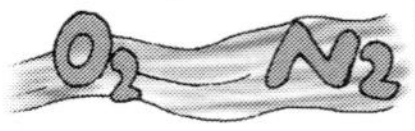

____

5. 

About $\frac{2}{3}$rd of elephants have tusks. How many elephants with tusks will be there in a herd of 75 elephants?

____

6. The planet Uranus has 27 known moons. The dwarf planet Pluto has $\frac{1}{9}$th of this number. How many moons does Pluto have?

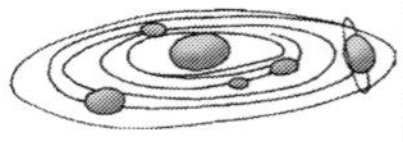

____

7. 

The expected life span of a dog is about 14 years. How old is a dog that has lived $\frac{2}{7}$th of the expected life span?

____

PROBLEM SOLVING

DOES THE SENTENCE MAKE SENSE?

Read the statements below and say 'yes' if they make sense. Say 'no' if they do not, and also explain why.

1. Two cooks together peeled a bag of potatoes. One cook peeled $\frac{4}{9}$ of the potatoes and the other peeled $\frac{7}{9}$ of the potatoes.

2. There are 12 heavy books on the shelf. Amin carries $\frac{1}{2}$ of the books, Mina carries $\frac{1}{3}$ of the books and Purva carries $\frac{1}{4}$ of the books.

3. Maulik has 12 stamps and Jaideep has 18 stamps. Maulik gives Jaideep half his stamps. Jaideep gives Maulik half his stamps. Jaideep gets less stamps than he gives.

4. An aeroplane was flying from Hyderabad to Visakhapatnam. Half way through, the pilot realised that he did not have enough fuel to get to Visakhapatnam. So he flew back to Hyderabad.

5. Out of 20 people in park, $\frac{1}{2}$ were children and $\frac{3}{4}$ were wearing spectacles.

6. Shikha ate $\frac{3}{5}$ of an apple. Avinash ate $\frac{3}{5}$ of another apple. Shikha ate more.

7. Three friends were watching a TV programme. Amrish saw $\frac{1}{2}$ of it, Avantika saw $\frac{1}{2}$ of it and Saumya saw $\frac{1}{2}$ of it.

8. A sandwich was cut into 4 quarters. Amod ate one quarter, Alicia ate one quarter and Azim ate one half.

HIGHER ORDER THINKING SKILLS

1. Find the fractions:

(a) Fraction A + Fraction B = $\frac{4}{5}$

Fraction A – Fraction B = $\frac{2}{5}$

Fraction A = ________________

Fraction B = ________________

(b) Fraction C + Fraction D = $\frac{5}{7}$

Fraction C – Fraction D = $\frac{1}{7}$

Fraction C = ________________

Fraction D = ________________

2. A cycle shop has 18 tricycles. $\frac{1}{3}$ of them are red. $\frac{1}{2}$ of them are blue. The rest are yellow. How many yellow tricycles are in the shop?

____

3. 27 smaller cubes have been used to make this large cube. It has been painted blue from the outside. What fraction of the smaller cubes
   (a) have paint on 3 sides?
   (b) have paint on 2 sides?
   (c) have paint on 1 sides?
   (d) have no paint at all ?

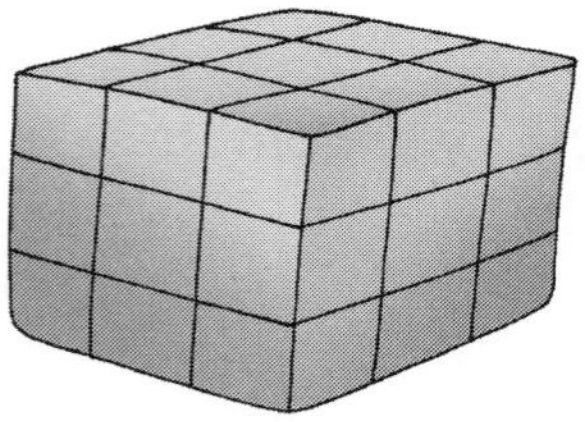

____

4. On a 100 m race track, hurdles were placed every 10m not including the start and the finish points. How many hurdles were needed? How many will be needed for a 200 m track?

____

MENTAL MATHS

1. $\frac{1}{4}$ of an hour = ________ minutes
2. $\frac{1}{3}$ of a day = ________ hours
3. $\frac{1}{2}$ of a 70 cm long ribbon = ________ cm
4. Write $\frac{5}{5}$ in another way. ________
5. Give two more like fractions for $\frac{3}{4}$.
6. Arrange $\frac{3}{11}, \frac{5}{11}, \frac{1}{11}, \frac{10}{11}$ in ascending order. ______________
7. Arrange $\frac{8}{13}, \frac{6}{13}, \frac{5}{13}, \frac{9}{13}$ in descending order. ______________
8. $\frac{5}{9}$ $\square$ $\frac{7}{9}$ (use >, < or =)
9. $\frac{7}{13} - \frac{4}{13} =$ ________
10. $\frac{2}{3}$ of 30 = ________
11. $\frac{1}{5}$ of 500 ml = ________ ml
12. $\frac{1}{2} = \frac{\square}{4}$
13. $\frac{14}{19} - \frac{12}{19} =$ ________
14. $\frac{2}{5}$ of 45 = ________
15. $\frac{\square}{3} = \frac{2}{6}$
16. $\frac{1}{3}$ of a year = _____ months
17. $\frac{1}{3}$ of Rs 15 + $\frac{1}{2}$ of Rs 10 = Rs _____
18. $\frac{1}{8}$ of 80 cm – $\frac{1}{10}$ of 50 cm = ___ cm
19. If $\frac{1}{3}$ of a number is 10, what is the number?
20. $\frac{1}{2}$ of 1 m = ________ cm
21. $\frac{1}{3}$ dozen + $\frac{1}{4}$ dozen = ________
22. $\frac{2}{17} + \frac{4}{17} + \frac{7}{17} =$ ________
23. $\frac{4}{9} + \frac{\square}{9} = \frac{7}{9}$
24. $\frac{3}{11} + \frac{6}{11} =$ ________
25. $\frac{8}{13} - \frac{\square}{13} = \frac{4}{13}$
26. $\frac{1}{4}$ of 800 g = ________
27. $\frac{2}{3}$ of 60 – $\frac{1}{4}$ of 60 = ________
28. $\frac{1}{10}$ of a rupee = ______ paise
29. $\frac{17}{17} =$ (give a whole number)
30. $7\frac{3}{8}$ (give an improper fraction)
31. $\frac{7}{19} - \frac{5}{19} =$ ________
32. $\frac{12}{12}$ $\square$ $\frac{15}{15}$ (use >, < or =)

Students may do only 8 sums at a time.

TEST YOUR SKILLS*

Tick (✓) the correct answer for each question.

1. 4356 ÷ 9
   (a) 494
   (b) 584
   (c) 484
   (d) 504

2. 765 ÷ 26
   (a) Q 28 R 37
   (b) Q 19 R 23
   (c) Q 29 R 11
   (d) Q 28 R 17

3. Name all the factors of 30.
   (a) 3, 10, 15, 2, 30
   (b) 1, 2, 3, 5, 6, 10, 15, 30
   (c) 2, 5, 6, 10, 15
   (d) 5, 6, 10, 15, 30

4. Give the common factors of 12 and 15.
   (a) 1, 2, 3
   (b) 1, 3
   (c) 1, 5, 3
   (d) 1, 4, 3

5. Find the first two common multiples of 3 and 5.
   (a) 13, 15
   (b) 10, 30
   (c) 15, 30
   (d) 30, 60

6. What is $\frac{23}{7}$ as a mixed number?
   (a) $2\frac{3}{7}$ (b) $3\frac{2}{7}$
   (c) $2\frac{3}{9}$ (d) $3\frac{2}{9}$

7. Rearrange in decreasing order. $\frac{2}{7}$ $\frac{5}{7}$ $\frac{1}{7}$ $\frac{6}{7}$
   (a) $\frac{6}{7}$ $\frac{5}{7}$ $\frac{1}{7}$ $\frac{2}{7}$
   (b) $\frac{6}{7}$ $\frac{5}{7}$ $\frac{2}{7}$ $\frac{1}{7}$
   (c) $\frac{1}{7}$ $\frac{2}{7}$ $\frac{5}{7}$ $\frac{6}{7}$
   (d) $\frac{2}{7}$ $\frac{1}{7}$ $\frac{5}{7}$ $\frac{6}{7}$

8. What is $\frac{2}{5}$ of 45?
   (a) 18
   (b) 9
   (c) 20
   (d) 15

9. $\frac{11}{19} + \frac{5}{19} = ?$
   (a) $\frac{16}{38}$ (b) $\frac{6}{19}$
   (c) $\frac{15}{19}$ (d) $\frac{16}{19}$

10. 5 children contributed equally to buy a gift for a friend. If the gift costs Rs 227.50, how much did each child give?
    (a) Rs 40.50
    (b) Rs 50
    (c) Rs 45
    (d) Rs 45.50

11. 765 bottles were put in crates of 24 each. How many crates will be needed for all the bottles?
    (a) 32 crates
    (b) 31 crates
    (c) 33 crates
    (d) 30 crates

12. A maths test paper had $\frac{3}{8}$ questions on calculation sums and $\frac{5}{8}$ on problem sums. How much more of the paper was on problem sums?
    (a) $\frac{8}{8}$ (b) $\frac{2}{8}$
    (c) $\frac{15}{8}$ (d) $\frac{2}{0}$

*This is for chapters 4,5,6.

Shapes, Space and Patterns

STRAIGHT LINES

Draw over the dotted lines using red for horizontal, blue for vertical and green for slanting lines.

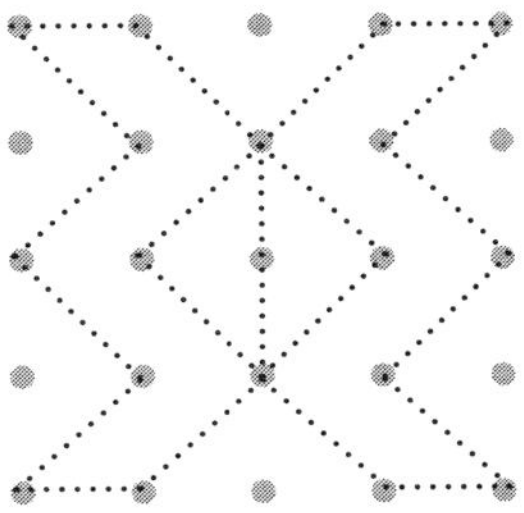

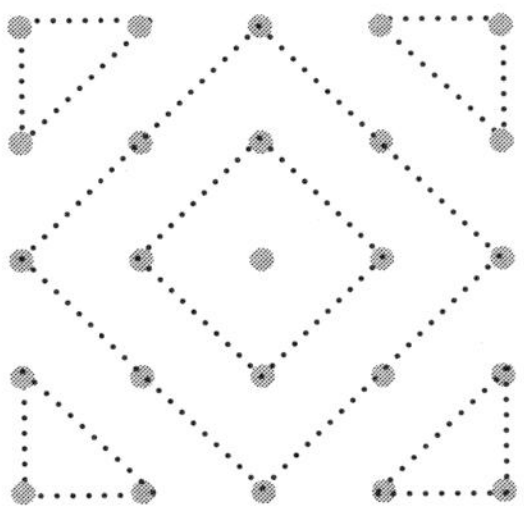

This worksheet integrates Mathematics and Art.

Half of the following designs have been done. Complete the other half.

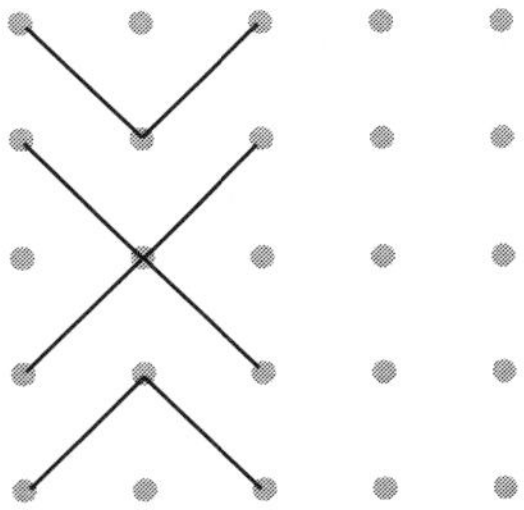

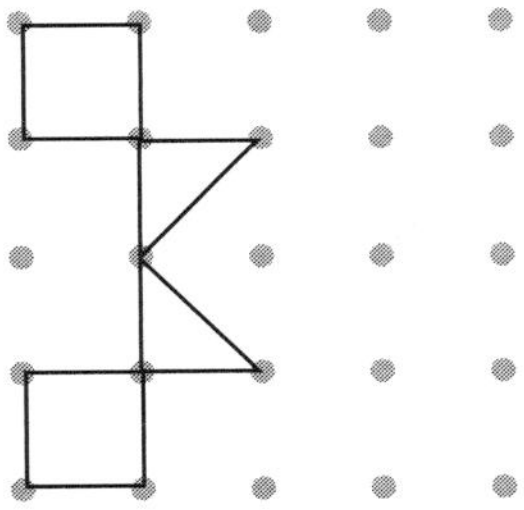

Make your own designs using horizontal, vertical and slanting lines.

Drawing circles

Use your compass. Use points A to E to draw circles of different radii. The circles should not touch each other.

C

B

A

D

E

Use your compass. Use points A to F to draw circles. They should not overlap the circle in the centre, but may touch it. Circles A to F may overlap each other.

C

B

D

A

E

F

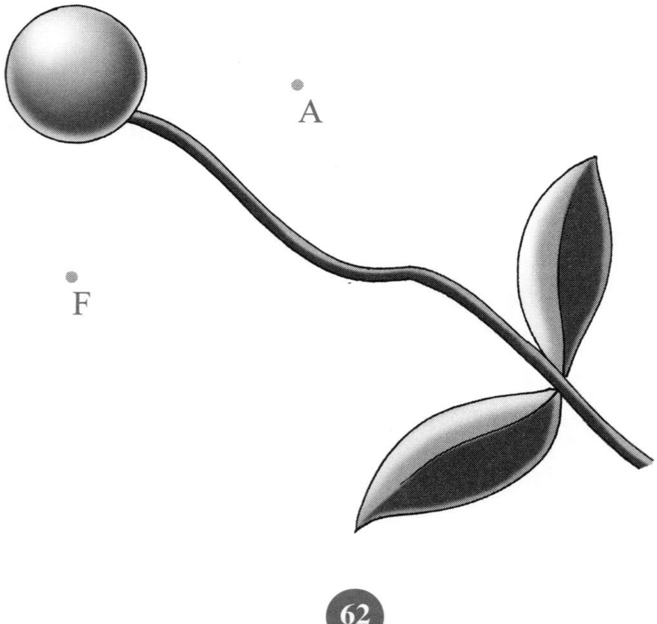

The dotted lines are the lines of symmetry. Draw the other half of the shape.

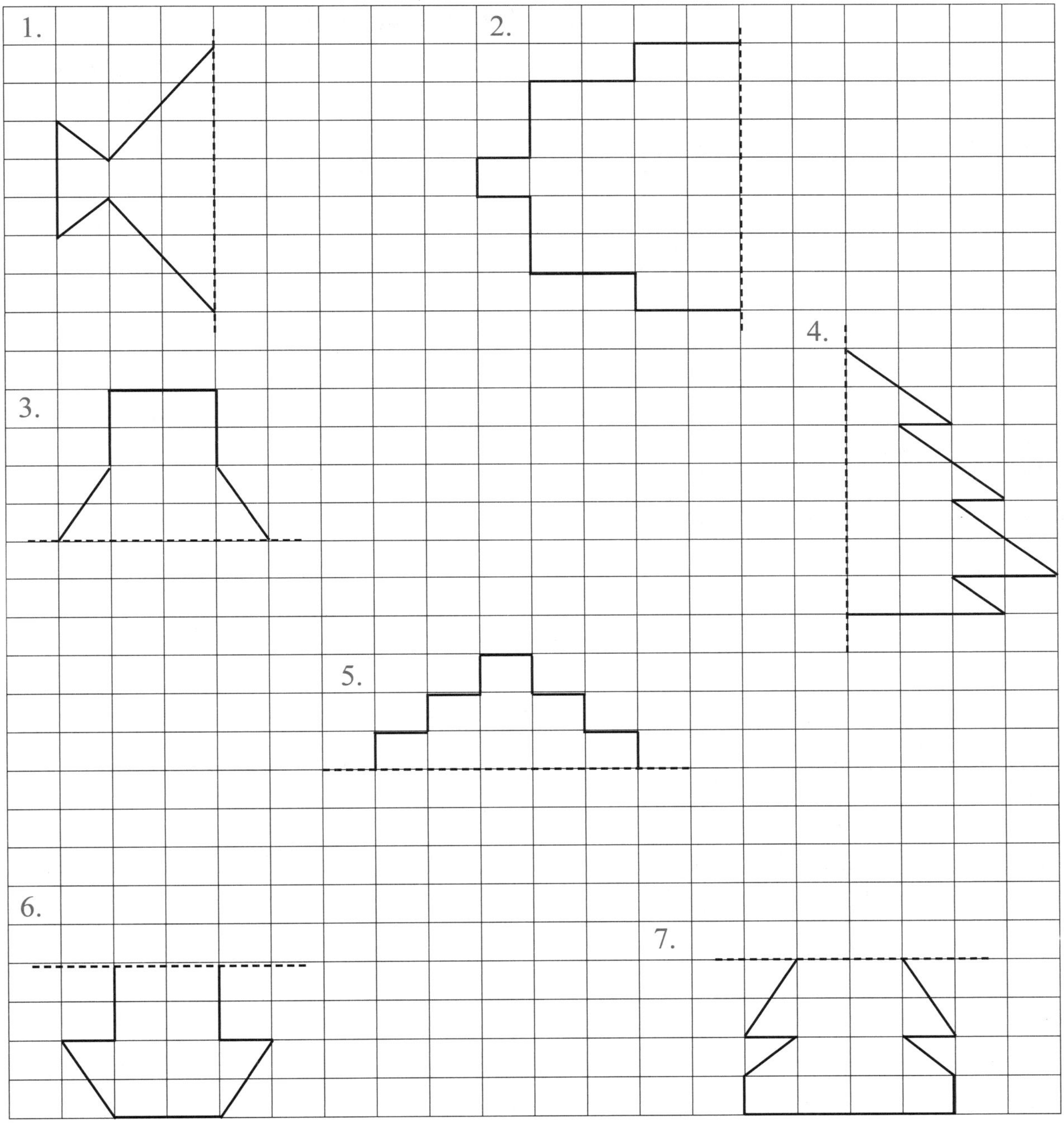

Teacher's tip:
Students may use their own slates and draw out solutions for questions that the teacher may write on the blackboard based on horizontal, vertical, slanting lines, symmetrical shapes and patterns. Groups of students may show one answer at a time and hold it up for the teacher to see.

PATTERNS

Tiling patterns

Colour according to the code. Once you see the pattern, colour it yourself.
R-red, Y-yellow, B-blue, G-green.

1.

B	B	B	R	R	R	Y	Y	Y	B	B	B	R	R	R					
Y	B	B	B	R	R	R	Y	Y	Y	B	B	B	R	R	R				
Y	Y	B	B	B	R	R	R	Y	Y	Y	B	B	B						

2.

R	R	R	G	R	G	R	R	R	G										
G	R	G	G	R	G	G	R	G	G										
G	R	G	R	R	R	G	R	G											

3.

Y	Y	Y	B	Y	Y	Y	B												
Y	Y	Y	B	Y	Y	Y	B												
Y	B	B	B	Y	B	B	B												
Y	B	B	B	Y	B	B	B												

4.

B	B	Y	B	Y	Y	Y	G	Y	G	G	G	R	G	R	R	R	B	R	B
B	R	B	B	B	Y	B	Y	Y	Y	G	Y	G	G	G	R	G	R	R	R
R	R	R	B	R	B	B	B	Y	B	Y	Y	Y	G	Y	G	G	G	R	G
G	R	G	R	R	R	B	R	B	B	B	Y	B	Y	Y	Y	G	Y	G	G
Y	G	G	G	R	G	R	R	R	B	R	B	B	B	Y	B	Y	Y	Y	G

HIGHER ORDER THINKING SKILLS

1. Make a different triangle in each of these.

2. Make a different quadrilateral in each of these.

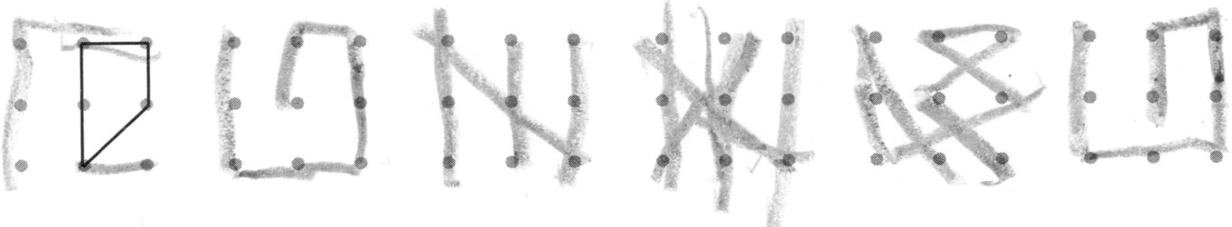

3. How many rectangles and triangles are there in this shape?

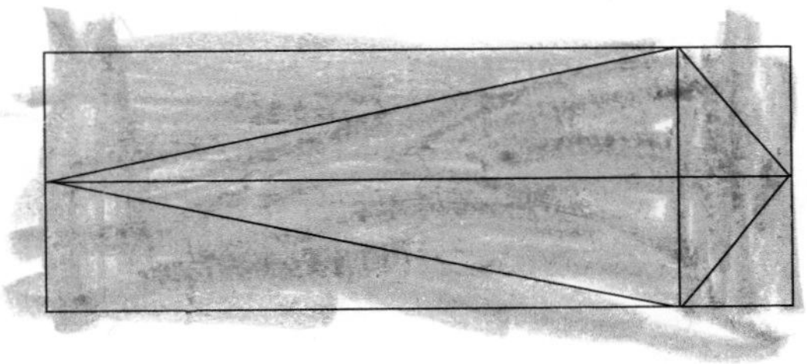

rectangles = __________

triangles = __________

4. Which of these shapes can you draw using one continuous line without retracing your lines or lifting your pencil?

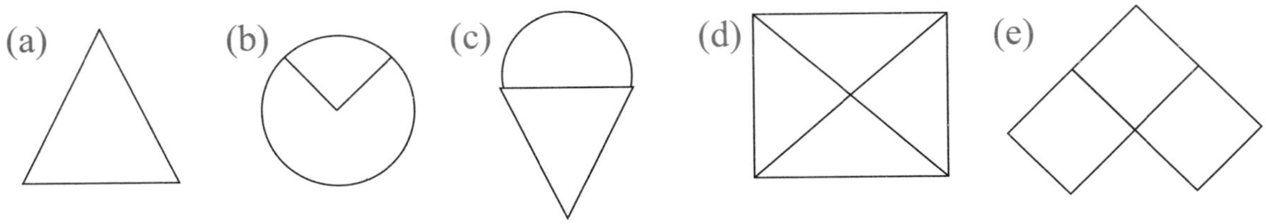

5.

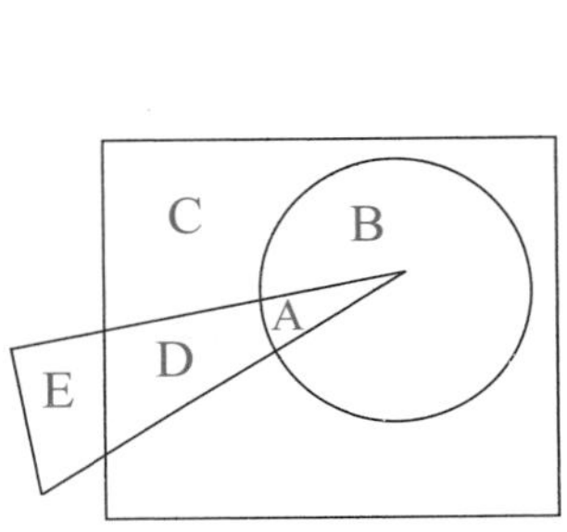

Say true or false.

(a) B is in the rectangle and circle. __________

(b) A is in the triangle and circle only. __________

(c) E is in the triangle only. __________

(d) C is in the rectangle only. __________

(e) D is in the triangle only. __________

QUIZ !

1. Give another name for the distance from the boundary of a circle to its centre. _____
2. The diameter is twice the radius. True or false? ________________
3. Given another name for the mirror image of a shape. ________________
4. What is the radius of a circle whose diameter is 70 cm? ________________
5. What is the diameter of a circle whose radius is 45 m? ________________
6. What is a special rectangle with four equal sides called? ________________
7. What is a polygon with four line segments called? ________________
8. Name the polygon with three sides. ________________
9. All quadrilaterals are rectangles. True or False? ________________
10. What is the length of the boundary of a circle called? ________________

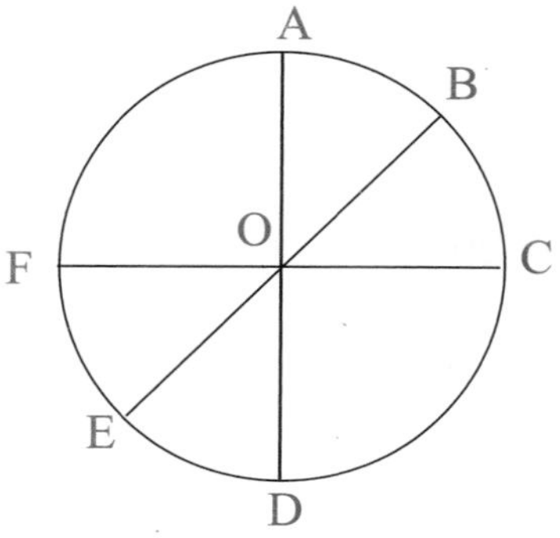

11. In the circle given alongside:
   (a) Name all the diameters.
   (b) Name all the radii.
   (c) Name the centre of the circle.
   (d) ______, ______, ______, ______, ______, ______ are points on the circumference.

12. Circle the shapes that are reflections of each other.

(a) 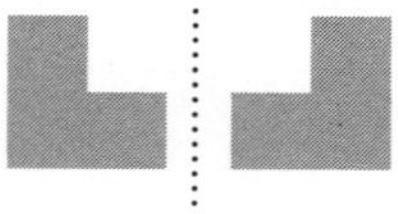 (b)  (c) 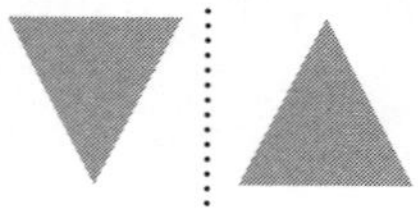 (d) 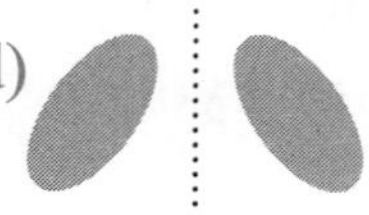

13. Complete the patterns.

(a)  ________________

(b) 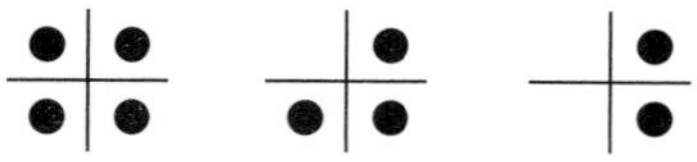 ________________

(c) 14, 17, 16, 19, 18, ________________

(d) 2, 3, 5, 8, 12, 17, ________________

(e) 10, 21, 32, 43, 54, ________________

Measurement

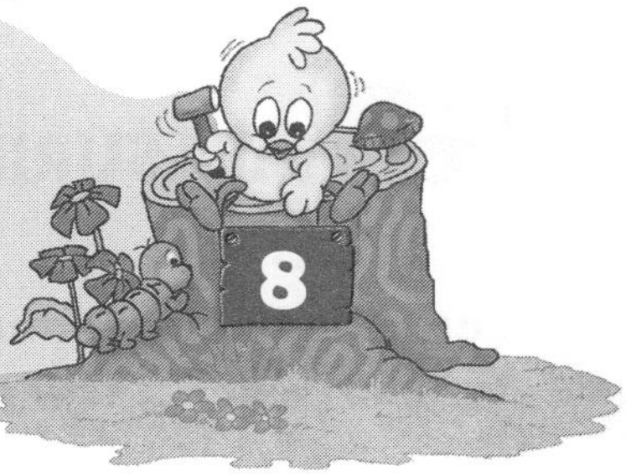

DRAWING LINES TO MEASUREMENT

Use a ruler to draw these symbols according to the measurements given.

(a) 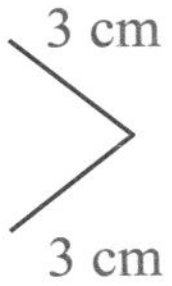

(b) 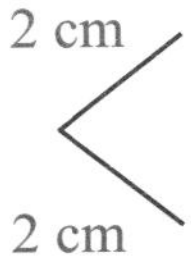

(c) 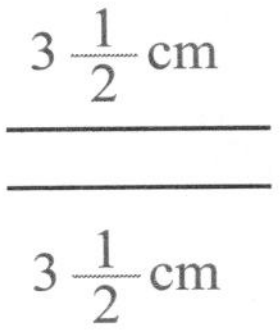

(d) 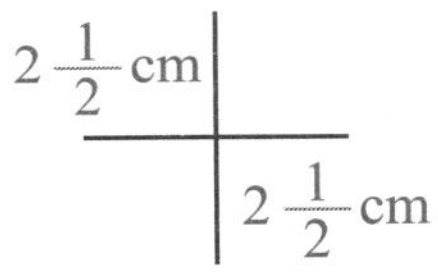

(e) 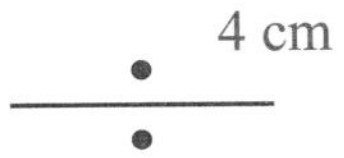

(f) 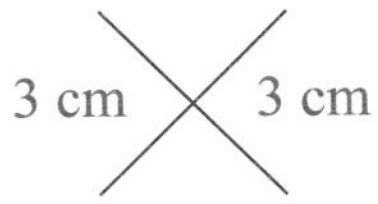

(g) 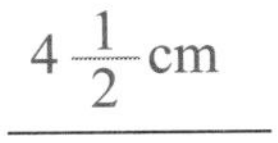

Turn the book around.
Measure each darkened line to the nearest cm or half cm.

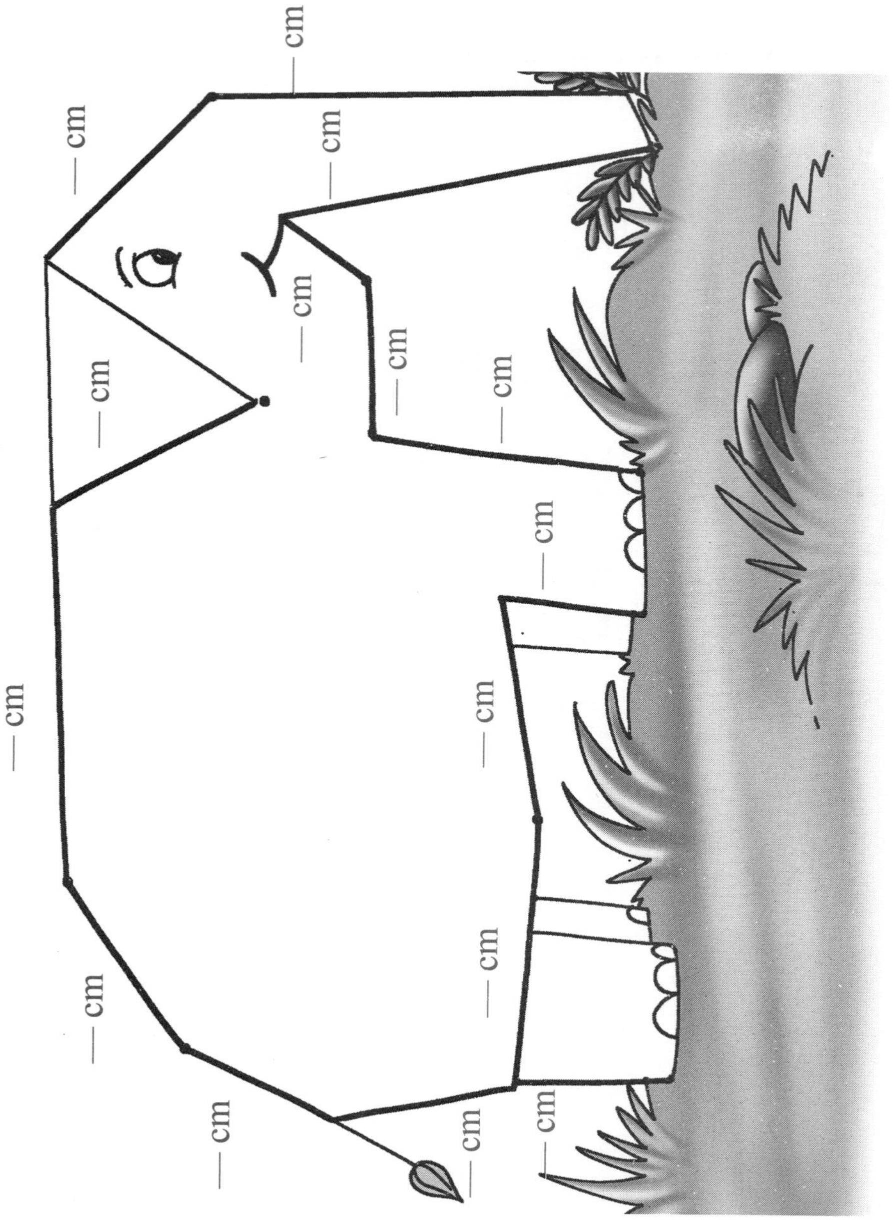

Teacher's tip:

This worksheet sheet may be used as a peer assessment exercise. Other students may check the length of the lines measured by their partners.

PROBLEM SOLVING

PRACTICE WORKSHEET

MEASUREMENT OF LENGTH

Match the questions to their answers.

1.		Pushpa jogged 500 m and walked 250 m. How much further does she have to go to complete a kilometre?
2.		The length of a swimming pool is 50 m. What distance will someone who has done two lengths, have swum?
3.		Shalini needs $2\frac{1}{2}$ m of cloth to make a *kameez*. How much is that in cm?
4.	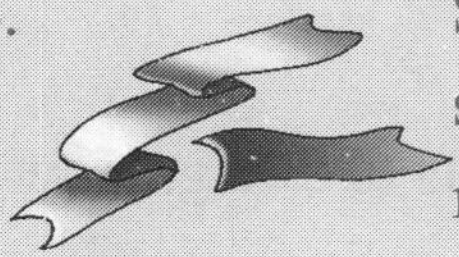	Sushmita buys 2 m of ribbon of which she uses only 175 cm. How much ribbon is still left with her?
5.		The blue whale is about 30 m in length. The killer whale is about 9 m in length. What is the difference in their lengths?
6.	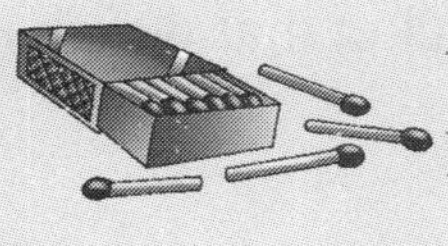	A matchstick is about 5 cm long. What will be the length of 25 matchsticks kept in a row? Give your answer in cm.
7.		A kangaroo hops 3 m at a time. How far would he have gone if he hopped 33 times?

25 cm
250 cm
125 cm
250 m
100 m
99 m
21 m

PRACTICE WORKSHEET

PROBLEM SOLVING

MEASUREMENT OF MASS

This is Minoo's practice paper. She has made some mistake in each answer. Sometimes she has made a calculation error, sometimes she has written the wrong word. Find each mistake and correct it.

Name: Minoo Class IV A

1. A gold coin weighs 8 g. Will the weight of 100 gold coins be more or less than a kg? How much more or less?

   Answer: 200 g more.

2. A kilo of peas costs Rs 18. What will be the cost of 2 kilos? What will half a kilo cost?

   Answer: 2 kg will cost Rs 38. Half a kilo will cost Rs 9.

3. A toothpaste of 50 g comes free with a larger toothpaste of 200 g. If you buy two such larger toothpastes, how much toothpaste will you have?

   Answer: 250 g

4. You have 1 kg of mango pulp. You want to freeze it in smaller packets of 200 g. How many such packets can you make?

   Answer: 20 packets

5. 20 kg of luggage are permitted on a plane. If your bag weighs $22\frac{1}{2}$ kg, how much excess are you carrying? Give your answer in g.

   Answer: $2\frac{1}{2}$ kg

6. A tea bag weighs about 5 g. How many tea bags will be there in a packet that weighs 100 g?

   Answer: 20 packets

7. A laptop weighs about $2\frac{1}{2}$ kg. The laptop bag weighs about 750 g. What weight will a person carrying the laptop in the bag, be carrying in kg?

   Answer: 3 kg.

PROBLEM SOLVING

PRACTICE WORKSHEET

MEASUREMENT OF CAPACITY

1. A one litre packet of milk has 475 mℓ left in it. How much of the milk was used?

   ____

2. 

   Two mugs with 450 mℓ and 560 mℓ juice were poured into another bottle of 1 litre. Will all the juice fit into the bottle?

   ____

3. A flask with 215 mℓ squash was diluted with 300 mℓ water. How much liquid is in the flask now?

   ____

4. 

   A recipe needs 250 mℓ grape juice and 500 mℓ apple juice. If double the recipe has to be made, how much of each will be needed? Give your answer in litres.

   ____

5. Mrs Sharma wants to make $\frac{1}{2}$ litre of orange juice. If each orange gives her 50 mℓ juice, how many oranges will she need for half a litre?

   ____

6. Tell which of these statements can be possible.

   (a) I can drink 50 litres of milk in a day. NOT POSSIBLE

   (b) I need 100 mℓ of water to bathe. ______________________

   (c) A vase can hold 500 mℓ of water. ______________________

   (d) I made 50 mℓ of soup for the family dinner. ______________________

   (e) The fish bowl contains 3 litres of water. ______________________

   (f) The cat bowl has 200 mℓ milk. ______________________

   (g) An elephant can drink 75 litres of water a day. ______________________

   (h) The baby has 5 mℓ of medicine. ______________________

CONVERSIONS

THE METRIC SYSTEM WAS OFFICIALLY RENAMED IN 1960 AND GIVEN THE SYMBOL SI. WHAT IS ITS NEW NAME?

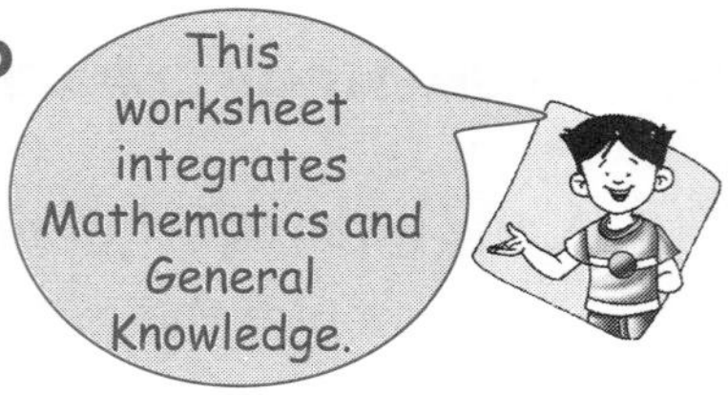
This worksheet integrates Mathematics and General Knowledge.

Fill in the blanks. Then fill in the letters next to each sum above the answers given below to find the answer to the question.

1.	475 cm = 4 m 75 cm	N
2.	250 mℓ = ____ ℓ	S
3.	6000 mℓ = ____ ℓ	O
4.	6 m = ____ cm	T
5.	3750 g = ____ kg	A
6.	4500 g = ____ kg	T
7.	805 cm = ____ m ____ cm	U
8.	$8\frac{1}{4}$ kg = ____ g	R
9.	5000 mℓ = ____ ℓ	L
10.	2 km = ____ m	N
11.	6500 g = ____ kg	E
12.	5500 m = ____ km	I
13.	$5\frac{1}{2}$ ℓ = ____ mℓ	N
14.	9 ℓ = ____ mℓ	T
15.	7500 mℓ = ____ ℓ	Y
16.	$1\frac{1}{4}$ ℓ = ____ mℓ	F
17.	7m 7 cm = ____ cm	N
18.	250 g = ____ kg	S
19.	8050 m = ____ km ____ m	S
20.	$8\frac{3}{4}$ kg = ____ g	T
21.	$8\frac{1}{2}$ km = ____ m	I
22.	9500 mℓ = ____ ℓ	M
23.	3m 15 cm = ____ cm	I
24.	2000 g = ____ kg	E
25.	6250 mℓ = ____ ℓ	A
26.	7000 m = ____ km	O

____ N ____ ____ ____ —

$5\frac{1}{2}$ km | 4m 75 cm | 9000 mℓ | 2 kg | 8250 g

707 cm | $6\frac{1}{4}$ ℓ | $4\frac{1}{2}$ kg | 8500 m | 7 km | 5500 mℓ | $3\frac{3}{4}$ kg | 5 ℓ

$\frac{1}{4}$ ℓ | $7\frac{1}{2}$ ℓ | 8 km 50 m | 600 cm | $6\frac{1}{2}$ kg | $9\frac{1}{2}$ ℓ

6 ℓ | 1250 mℓ

8m 5 cm | 2000 m | 315 cm | 8750 g | $\frac{1}{4}$ kg

HIGHER ORDER THINKING SKILLS

1. Observe the pattern in each pair. Work out two more such pairs.

$6 \times 6 = 36$	$9 \times 9 = 81$	$4 \times 4 = 16$		
$5 \times 7 = 35$	$8 \times 10 = 80$	$3 \times 5 = 15$		

2. A baby bird learnt to fly 4 m on the first day. After that it could fly double the distance each day. How far could it fly in a week?

____

3. A frog lived at the bottom of a well that was 8 m deep. How many days did he need to get out of the well if for every 3 m that he climbed up during the day, he slid back 1 m at night?

____

4. 

How much more should be poured into the bottle to make a litre?

____

5. A man has already walked 750 m. How much more should he walk to cover a km?

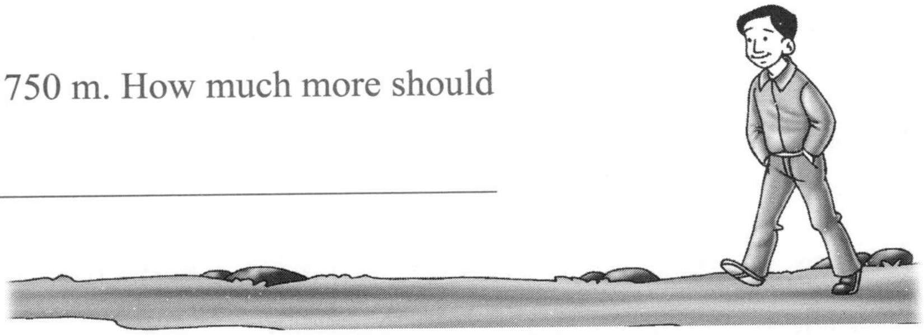

____

6. 

How much more should be added to make the weight of the oranges to 1 kg?

____

7. The top of a bookshelf is 175 cm away from a ceiling that is $3\frac{1}{2}$ m high. What is the height of the bookshelf?

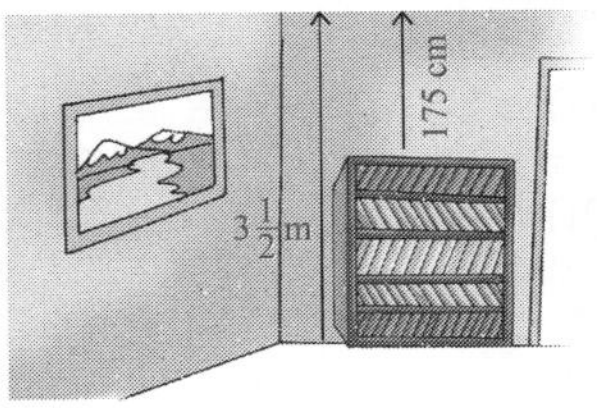

____

MENTAL MATHS

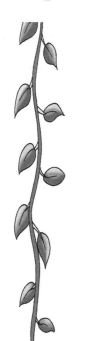

1. What unit would you use to weigh a worm? ________________
2. How many 5 cm lengths can you cut from a string 42 cm long? ________________
3. If you cut 15 cm from a 1m roll of ribbon, how much is left?
4. What is $\frac{1}{5}$ of a metre in cm? ________________
5. What is $\frac{2}{5}$ of 100ℓ ? ________________
6. What is $\frac{3}{4}$ of 160 kg? ________________
7. What unit will you use to weigh a potted plant? ______________
8. What is left if you take 500 g from 3 kg? ______________
9. How much should you drink from a $\frac{1}{2}$ ℓ bottle of water so that you are left with 250 mℓ in it? ______________
10. How many litres in 250 mℓ? ______________

Fill in the blanks:

11. 1512 m = _____ km _____ m
12. 202 cm = _____ m _____ cm
13. The height of a tall building : 300 _____
14. 1m 5 cm = _____ cm
15. The approximate weight of a table : 30 _____
16. 8100 m = _____ km _____ m
17. $8\frac{1}{2}$ km = _____ m
18. The petrol in a car tank: 40 _____
19. 1750 mℓ = _____ ℓ
20. $6\frac{1}{4}$ ℓ = _____ mℓ
21. 4750 g = _____ kg
22. The depth of a children's pool: $\frac{1}{2}$ _____
23. 4500 mℓ = _____ ℓ
24. $7\frac{1}{2}$ kg = _____ g
25. The weight of a *diya* : 5 ___
26. $9\frac{1}{4}$ kg = _____ g
27. The height of a vase : 20 ___
28. 5010 m = _____ km _____ m
29. The distance from my home to the railway station : 2 ______
30. The water in a glass: 200_______.

Students may do only 10 sums at a time.

Area and Perimeter

9

PERIMETER

Find the perimeter of these shapes. You will know you are right if the total of all the perimeters you get is 200 units.

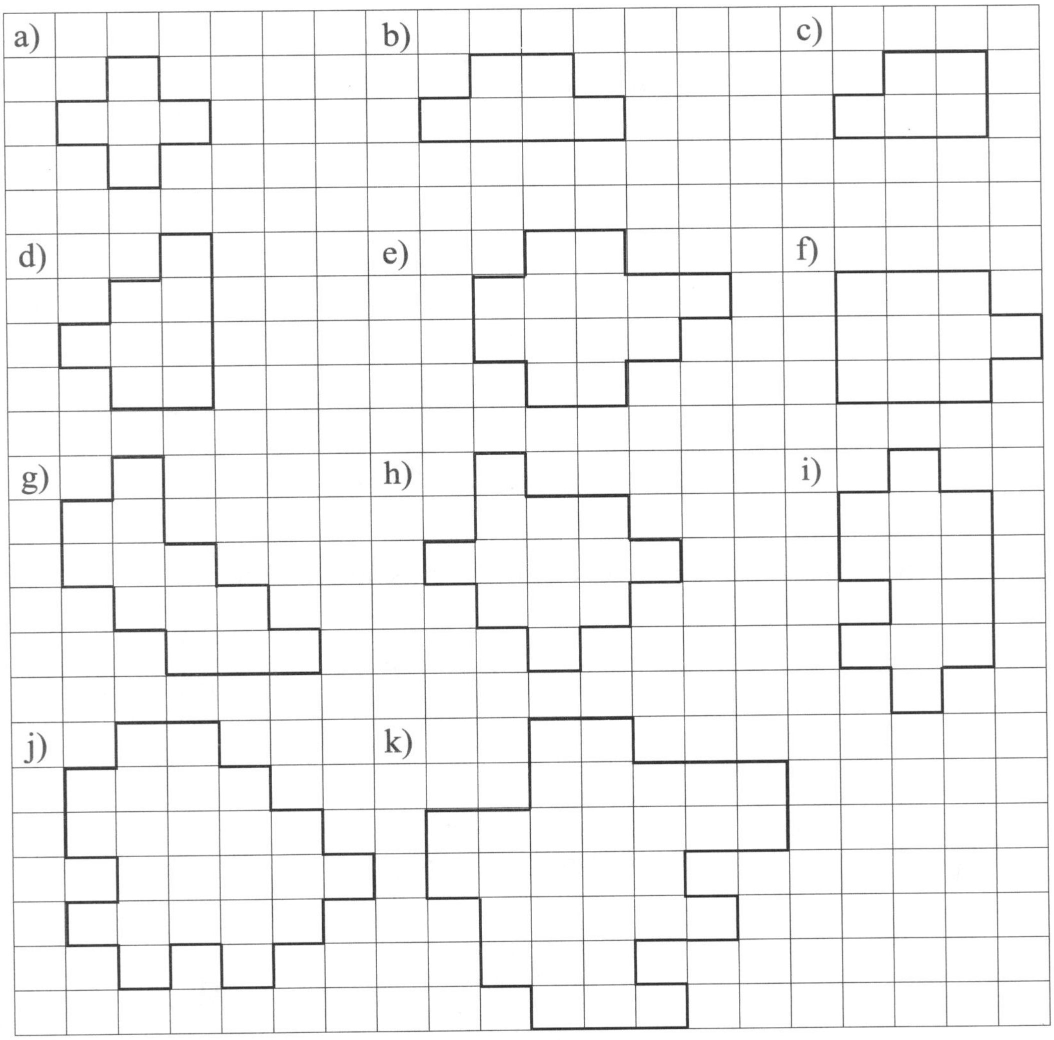

(a) _______ units (b) _______ units (c) _______ units (d) _______ units

(e) _______ units (f) _______ units (g) _______ units (h) _______ units

(i) _______ units (j) _______ units (k) _______ units

Total: _______ units

CALCULATING PERIMETER

1. Find the perimeter of each of the following figures.

(a)

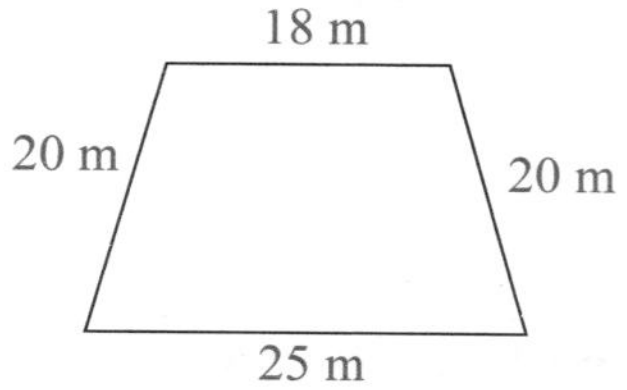

(b)

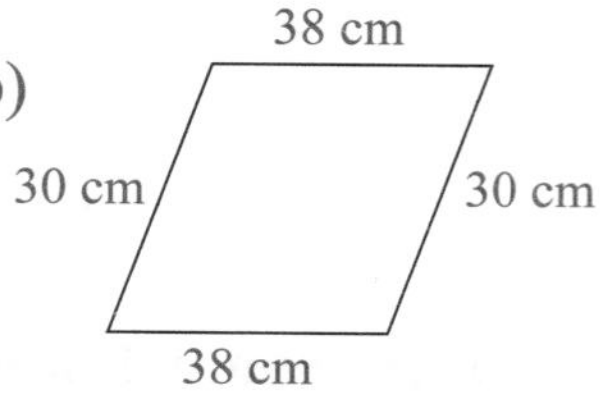

(c)

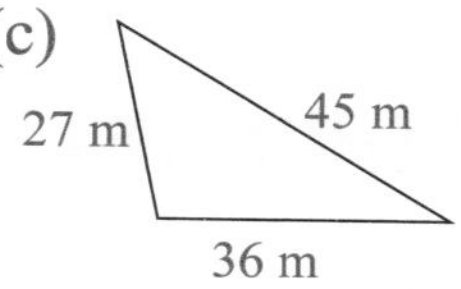

(d)

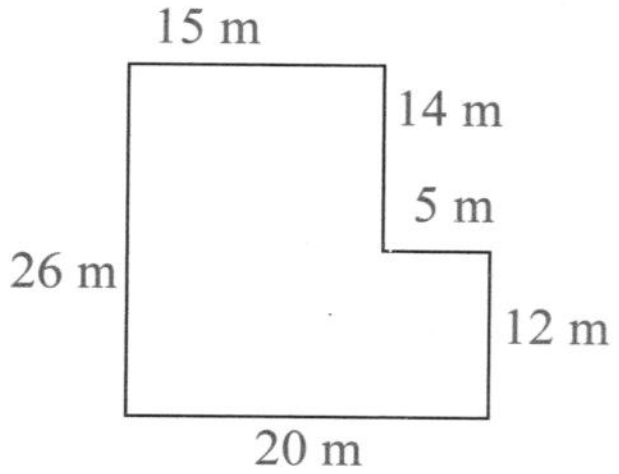

(e)

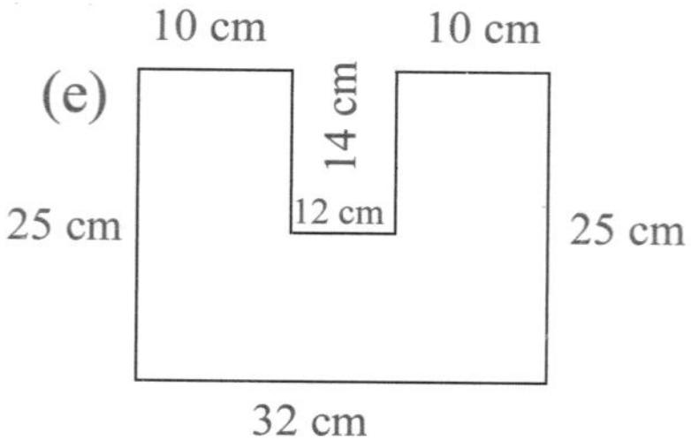

(f)

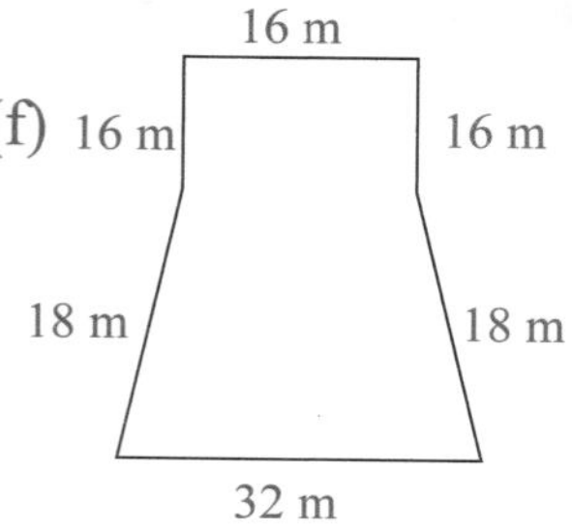

(g)

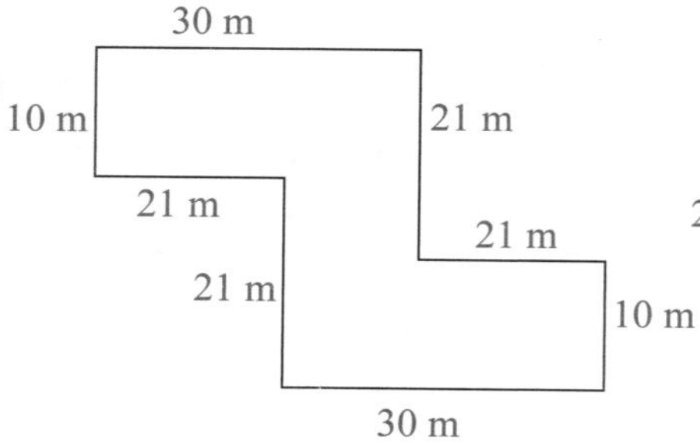

(h)

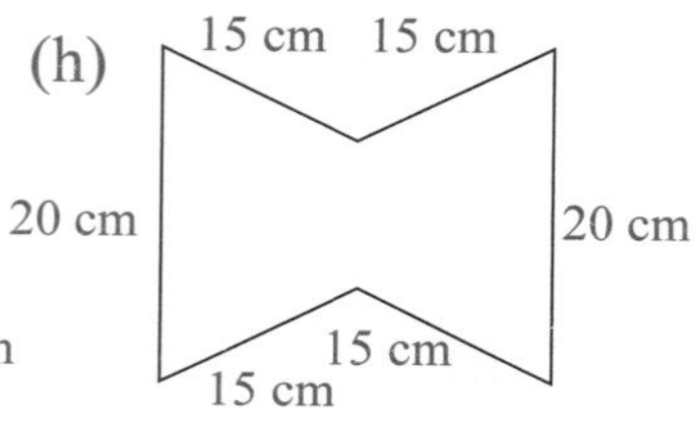

(i)

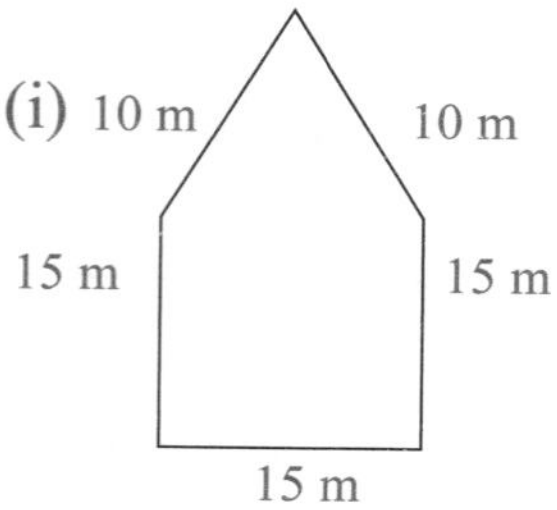

2. The perimeter of each shape is given. Find the missing length.

(a)

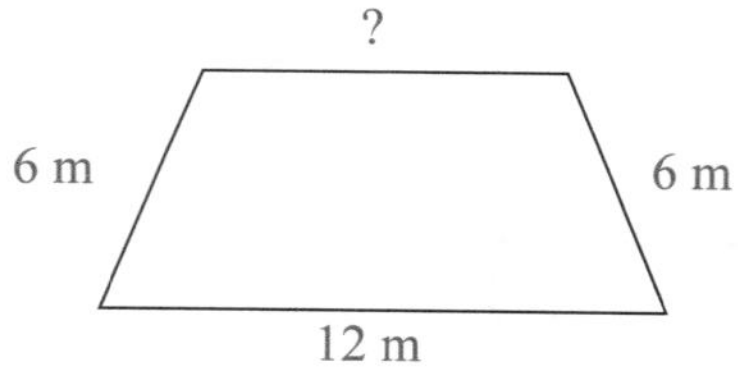

Perimeter - 31 m

(b)

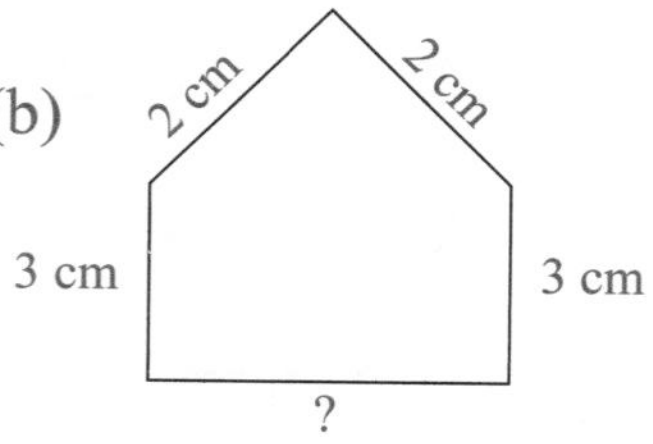

Perimeter : 15 cm

(c)

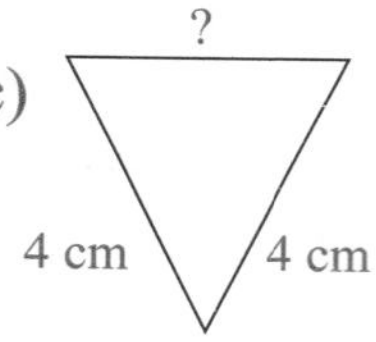

Perimeter : 11 cm

(d)

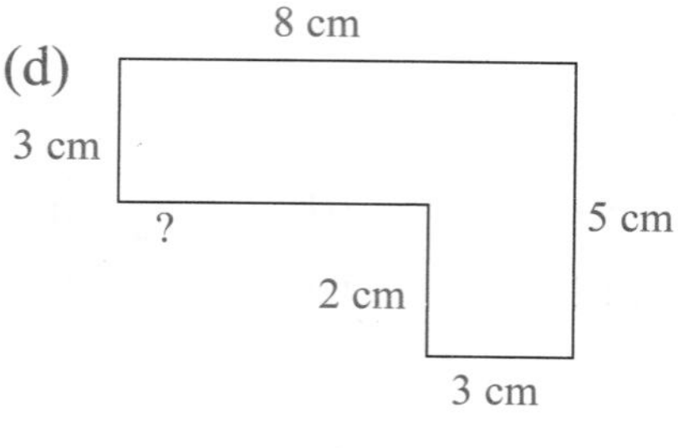

Perimeter : 26 cm

(e)

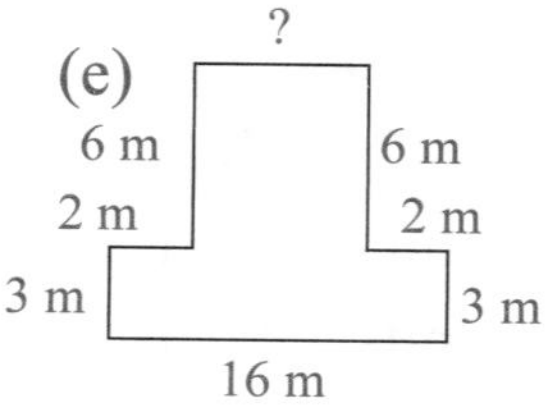

Perimeter : 50 m

(f)

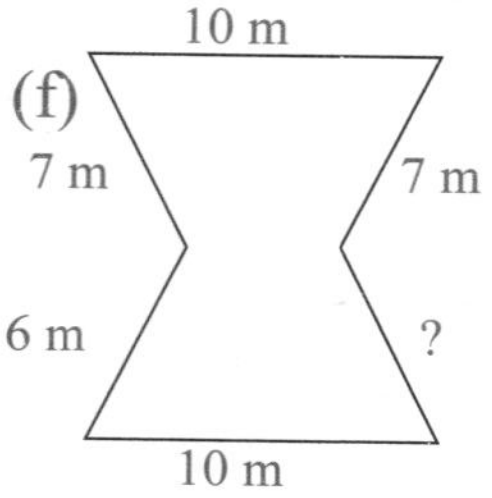

Perimeter : 46 m

Tick the shapes with an area of 5 sq units. Use the rest of the space to create other shapes with the same area. The area of each square being 1sq unit.

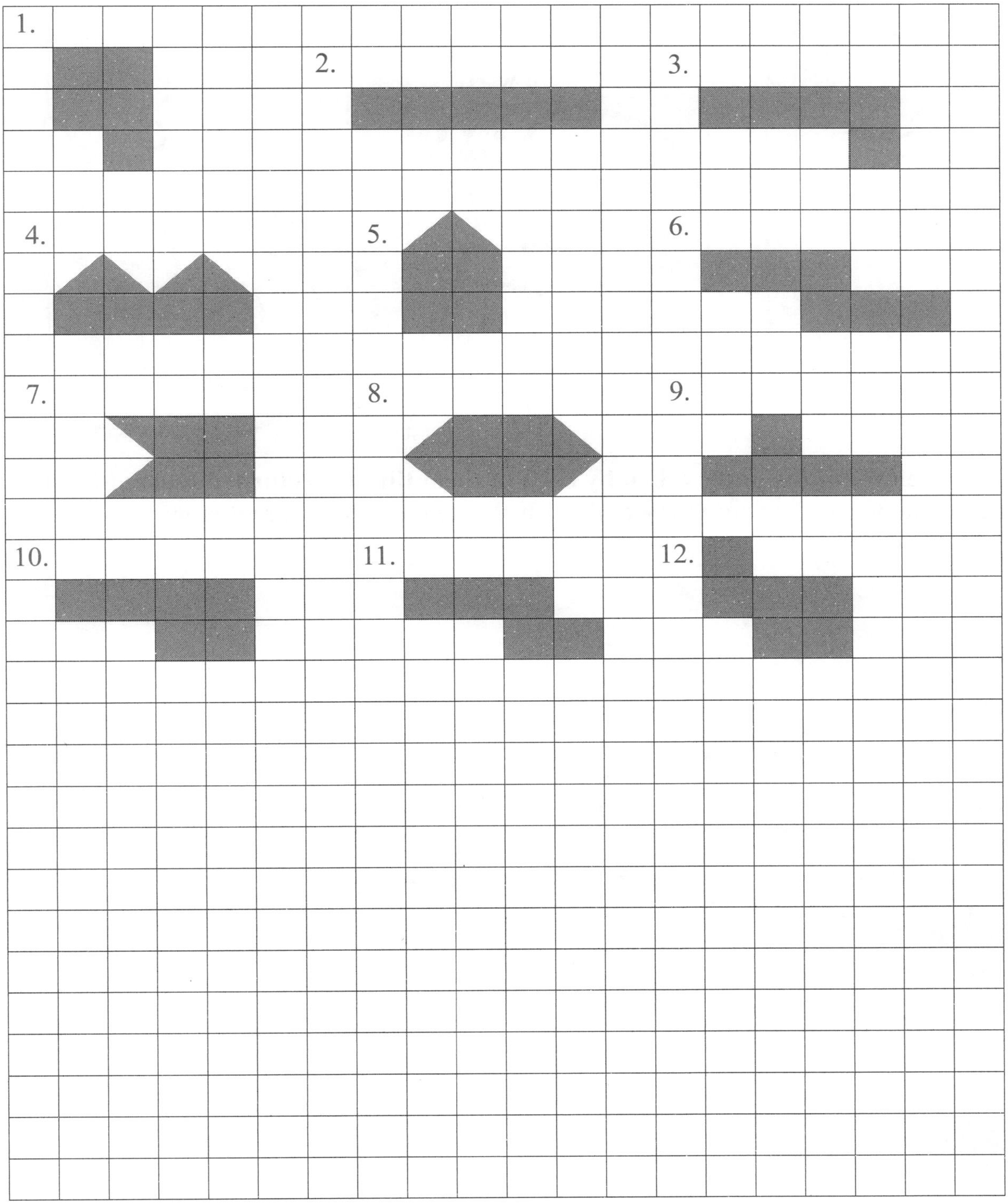

AREA AND PERIMETER OF IRREGULAR SHAPES

Papa Snail, Mama Snail and Baby Snail went out for a walk. Find out the area of each picture.

Given below are the paths taken by each of them till they returned home. Measure the perimeter of the route they took with the help of a string and ruler.

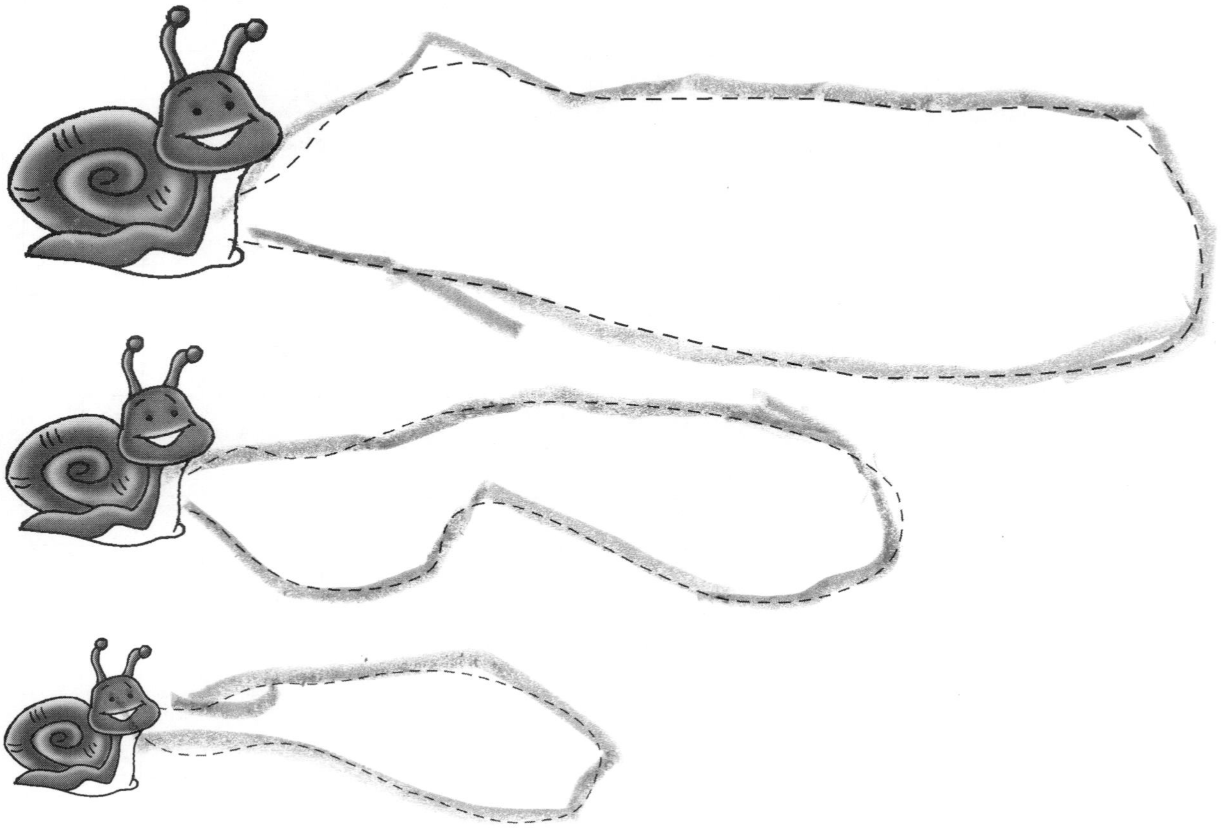

PROBLEM SOLVING

AREA AND PERIMETER

1. Hyacinth jogged four times around the park. If the perimeter of the park is 350 m, how far did she jog? Give your answer in km and m.

____

2. A square field is 150 m on each side. If you walk once around the field, how far would you have walked?

____

3. A rectangular pencil box has a perimeter of 28 cm. If one side is 10 cm, what will be the length of the other side? (Hint: Use a drawing.)

____

4. A square handkerchief has a perimeter of 60 cm. What is the length of each side of the handkerchief?

____

5. Look at the following diagram and answer the questions.

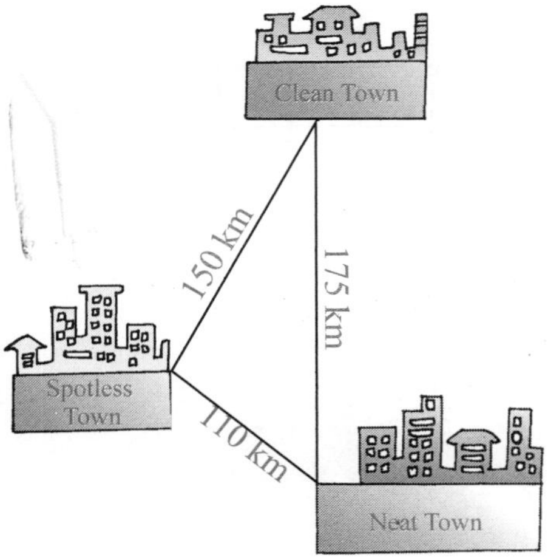

(a) What is the shortest distance from Spotless Town to Clean Town?

____

(b) How far is it from Neat Town to Spotless Town via Clean Town?

____

(c) How far will a person who is driving from Neat Town to Spotless Town to Clean Town and back to Neat Town have to travel?

____

d) Is Neat Town closer to Clean Town or Spotless Town?

____

HIGHER ORDER THINKING SKILLS

1. How many more tiles needed to cover this floor?

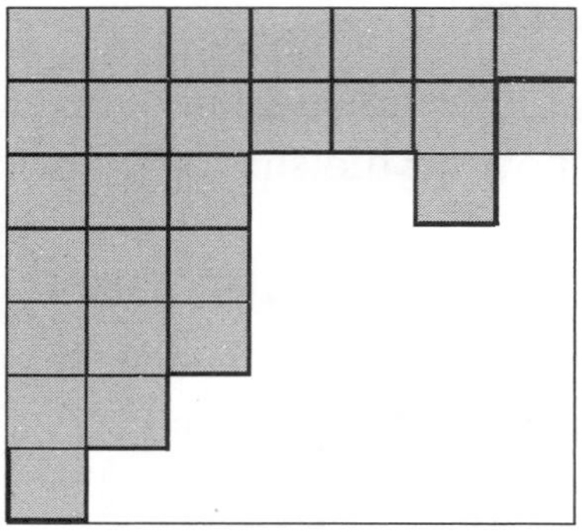

2. Will the snail find it shorter to go along the wall from A to B, or on the steps from A to B, or are both the same?

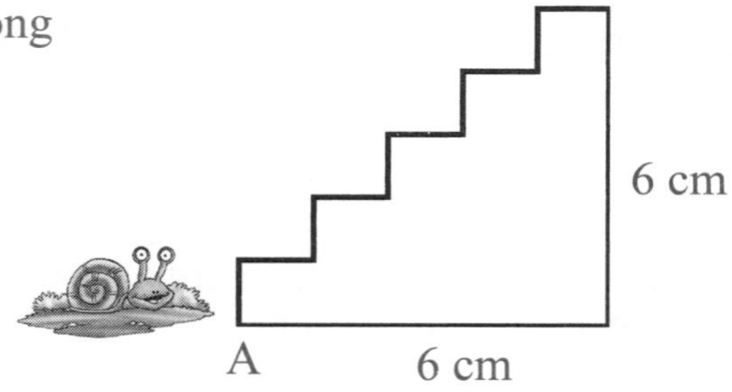

3. Use the grid below to draw two different shapes each with an area of 6 sq units and a perimeter of 12 units.

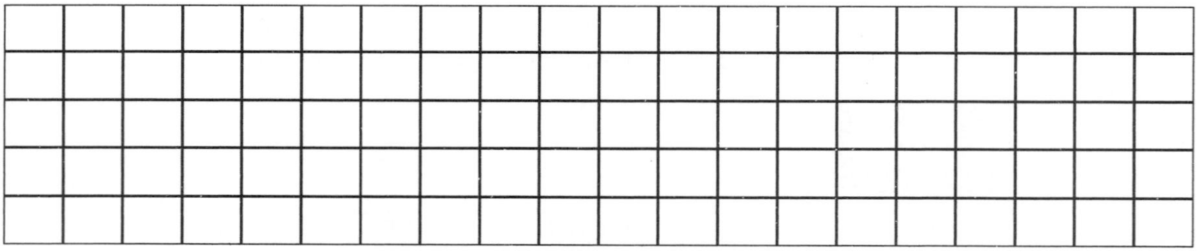

4. Abu wants to plant 4 saplings on each side of his rectangular garden. He has only 12 saplings. How will he do it?

5. Two brothers share a piece of land on which grows two apple trees, two banana trees and two coconut trees. Divide the land equally between them so that each brother has one of each kind of tree. Use the illustration alongside.

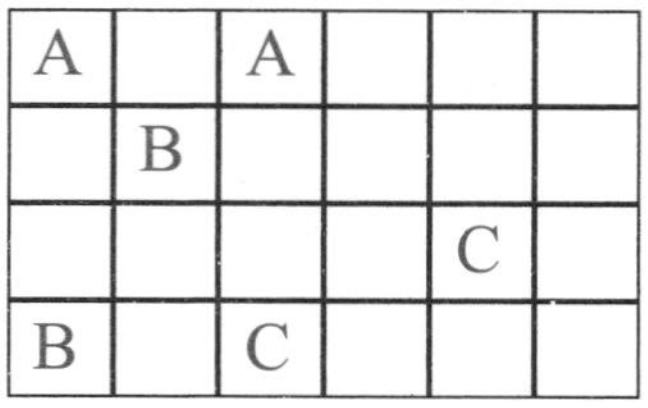

MENTAL MATHS

1. What is the distance around the edge of a figure called? __________
2. Area is the amount of surface a figure covers. True or false? __________
3. What is the perimeter of a square with sides 13 cm? __________
4. What is the perimeter of a rectangle with sides 1 m and 25 cm? ________
5. A quadrilateral with perimeter 160 cm, has three sides totalling 98 cm. What is the length of the fourth side? __________
6. Which is more, the area of your palm, or half the area of your mathematics book? __________
7. The perimeter of a square is 100 cm. What is the length of a side? ______
8. If one square shaped stamp covers 9 squares, what is its area? What is its perimeter? __________
9. What is the area of this shape?
10. What is the perimeter of this shape?

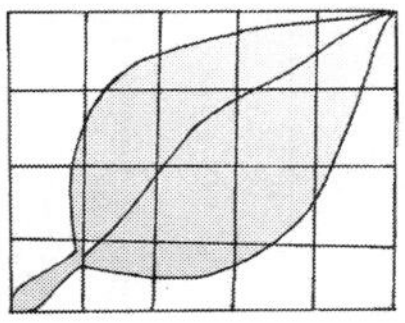

11. Round 3,45,287 to the nearest 1000.
12. 4098 – _______ = 3000
13. Add 750 to the product of 5 and 50. __
14. _______ × 100 = 45000
15. Give the Roman numeral for 19. ___
16. What is the double of Rs 7.50? ____
17. 3 less than a number is 17. What is the double of the number? ____
18. How many 50 p coins make Rs15? ___
19. Give the first 3 multiples of 8. ______
20. Give all the factors of 12. _________
21. 2 m 7 cm = _______ cm
22. 2500 mℓ = _______ ℓ
23. Weight of a pencil = 5 _______
24. Perimeter of a square of sides 5 cm = _______
25. What is 24 × 101?
26. Diameter of circle of radius 15 m = _______
27. Write $3\frac{4}{9}$ as an improper fraction.
28. $\frac{3}{4}$ of 40 = _______
29. $\frac{5}{7} + \frac{2}{7}$ = _______
30. $\frac{13}{17} - \frac{10}{17}$ = _______

Students may do only 10 sums at a time.

TEST YOUR SKILLS*

Tick (✓) the right answer for each question.

1. What kind of line is this?

   (a) horizontal
   (b) vertical
   (c) slanting
   (d) none of these

2. What is the diameter of a circle with radius 10 cm?
   (a) 5 cm
   (b) 15 cm
   (c) 20 cm
   (d) 25 cm

3. Which of these shapes is a reflection of .
   (a) 
   (b) 
   (c) 
   (d) 

4. What is the length of this line to the nearest $\frac{1}{2}$ cm.

   (a) $3\frac{1}{2}$ cm
   (b) $2\frac{1}{2}$ cm
   (c) 4 cm
   (d) $4\frac{1}{2}$ cm

5. 4500 m = ________ km
   (a) 4 km
   (b) $4\frac{1}{2}$ km
   (c) 45 km
   (d) 40 km

6. $6\frac{1}{2}$ litres = ________ mℓ
   (a) 6500 mℓ
   (b) 6250 mℓ
   (c) 6000 mℓ
   (d) 6750 mℓ

7. $3\frac{1}{4}$ kg = ________ g
   (a) 3250 g
   (b) 3000 g
   (c) 3750 g
   (d) 3500 g

8. Give the perimeter of this shape.
   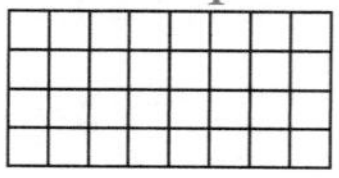
   (a) 24 units
   (b) 20 sq units
   (c) 22 units
   (d) 20 units

9. Give the missing length if the shape has a perimeter of 24 cm.
   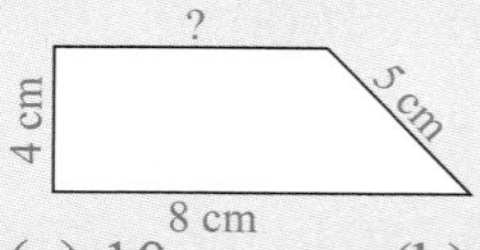

   (a) 10 cm (b) 7 cm
   (c) 6 cm (d) 8 cm

10. What is the area of this shape?
    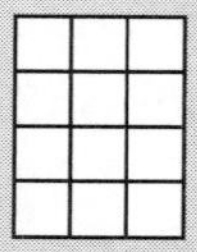
    (a) 14 units
    (b) 12 sq units
    (c) 12 units
    (d) 14 sq units

11. A pen holds 5 ml of ink. How many pens can be filled will 60 ml ink?
    (a) 12 pens
    (b) 300 pens
    (c) 65 pens
    (d) 55 pens

12. A straw is 15 cm long. How many straws will be needed to make a line 135 cm long?
    (a) 12 straws
    (b) 2025 straws
    (c) 9 straws
    (d) 150 straws

*This is for chapters 7,8,9.

Time

10

READING TIME TO THE EXACT MINUTE

1. Write the time below the clocks. One has been done for you.

(a)

1:12

(b)

____

(c)

____

(d)
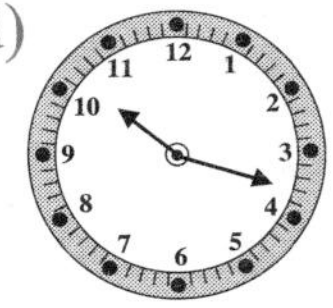
____

(e)

____

(f)

____

(g)

____

(h)

____

(i)
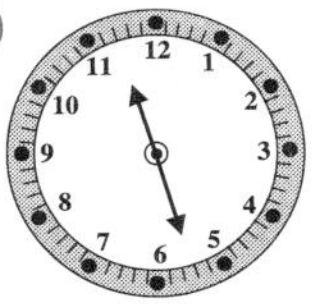
____

(j)

____

(k)

____

(l)

____

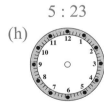

2. Draw the arms of the clock.

(a)
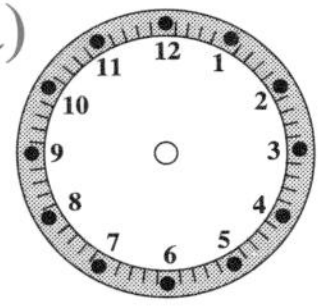
2 : 07

(b)
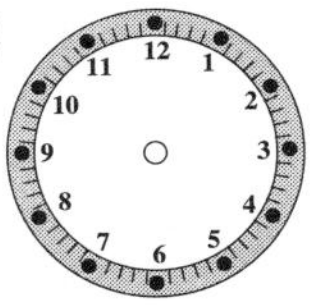
9 : 25

(c)
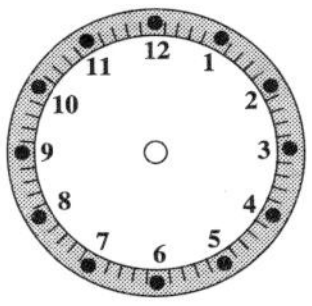
4 : 17

(d)
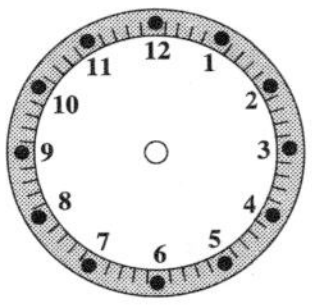
5 : 23

(e)
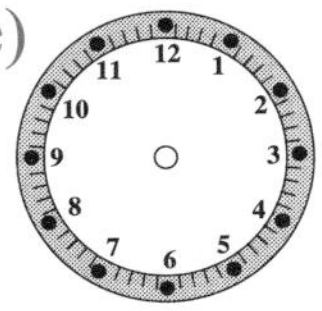
11 : 11

(f)
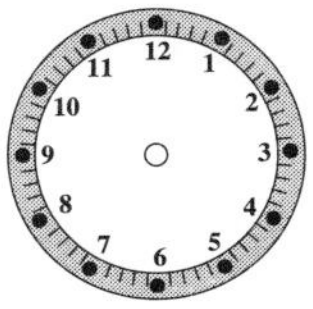
3 : 57

(g)
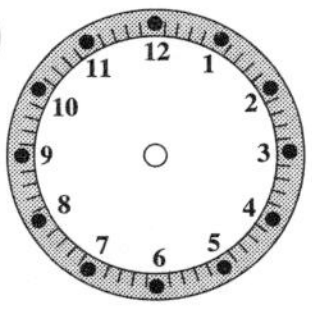
12 : 41

(h)
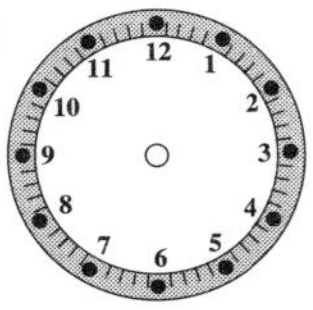
1 : 32

(i)
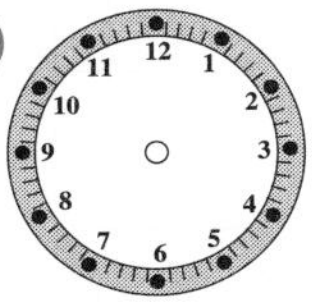
6 : 06

(j)
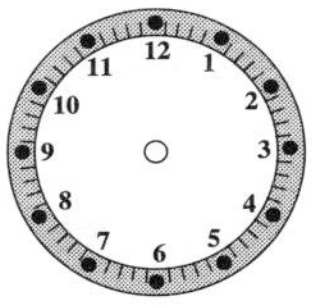
10 : 23

(k)
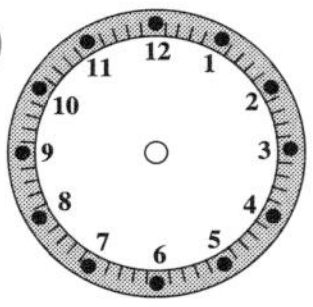
7 : 50

(l)
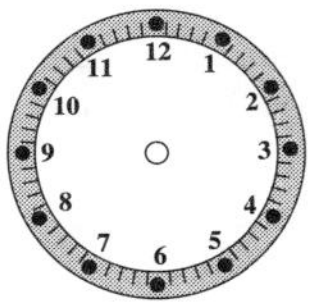
8 : 42

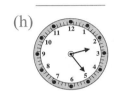

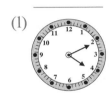

24-HOUR CLOCK

The table below show the flight timings from various cities. Fill in the boxes that are empty. Then calculate the length of each journey.

	12 hour clock		24 hour clock		Length of journey
From Delhi to	**Dep.**	**Arr.**	**Dep.**	**Arr.**	**Hours and minutes**
1. Srinagar	10:20 a.m.	12:40 p.m.	10:20 hrs	12:40 hrs	2hrs 20min
2. Jaipur			05:45 hrs	06:30 hrs	
3. Goa			10:05 hrs	14:15 hrs	
4. Bengaluru	8:10 p.m.	10:40 p.m.			
From Mumbai to					
5. Ahmedabad	12:35 p.m.	1:50 p.m.			
6. Kochi			12:15 hrs	14:00 hrs	
7. Hyderabad	6:45 p.m.	8:00 p.m.			
8. Bhopal			17:45 hrs	19:50 hrs	
From Chennai to					
9. Thiruvananthapuram	2:35 p.m.	4:10 p.m.			
10. Goa	5:55 a.m.	6:45 a.m.			
11. Kolkata			22:40 hrs	00:50 hrs	
12. Lucknow			07:15 hrs	13:35 hrs	
From Kolkata to					
13. Guwahati			10:55 hrs	12:10 hrs	
14. Hyderabad	6:15 a.m.	2:50 p.m.			
15. Bagdogra	11:20 a.m.	12:30 p.m.			
16. Delhi			20:35 hrs	23:05 hrs	

CALCULATING TIME

SELF-CORRECTING WORKSHEET

Fill in the blanks. Shade the answer in the box below to see a pattern.

1. 30 minutes after 7:30 p.m. _________
2. 30 minutes before 12 noon. _________
3. 1 hour after 6:05 a.m. _________
4. 1 hour before 1:05 p.m. _________
5. 45 minutes before 12:30 p.m. _________
6. 45 minutes after 11:15 p.m. _________
7. 2 hours 10 minutes after 10:15 p.m. _________
8. 2 hours 10 minutes after 10:50 p.m. _________
9. 3 hours before 7:10 a.m. _________
10. 1 hours 30 minutes after 3:35 a.m. _________
11. 1 hour 15 minutes before 5:15 p.m. _________
12. 2 hours 10 minutes after 9:10 p.m. _________
13. 3 hours after 12:20 p.m. _________
14. 3 hours after 1:40 a.m. _________
15. 2 hours before 7:05 p.m. _________
16. 2 hours before 1:15 a.m. _________
17. 1 hour 20 minutes before 12:20 a.m. _________
18. 1 hours 20 minutes after 10:40 a.m. _________

4:10 p.m.	11:45 a.m.	11:45 p.m.	8:00 p.m.	5:05 a.m.	4:00 p.m.	12:25 p.m.	11:20 p.m.	1:00 p.m.
11:00 p.m.	4:40 a.m.	7:05 a.m.	4:10 a.m.	5:05 a.m.	11:30 a.m.	3:20 p.m.	12 midnight	5:05 p.m.
12 noon	11:00 a.m.	1:00 a.m.	8:00 a.m.	12:25 a.m.	4:00 a.m.	12:05 p.m.	12:10 p.m.	11:15 p.m.

Mother Teresa dedicated her entire life to serving lepers, the homeless, the poorest of the poor, the sick and the dying on the streets of Kolkata. Her selfless work has been recognised and appreciated throughout the world.

The information below gives some of the important events in her life. The years are all mixed up. Plot the years and events on a timeline along with Mother Teresa's age at the time.

1910 – Born as Agnes Gonxhu Bejaxhiu in Skopje in the former Yugoslavia

1946 – Leaves the convent to serve the poor in Kolkata

1957 – Begins her work with lepers

1929 – Arrives in Kolkata, India

1979 – Awarded Nobel Peace Prize

1950 – Founds the Missionaries of Charity

1980 – Wins Bharat Ratna

1948 – Takes Indian citizenship

1997 – Dies in Kolkata

1928 – Becomes Roman Catholic Loretto nun and takes the name Sister Teresa.

This worksheet integrates Mathematics and History.

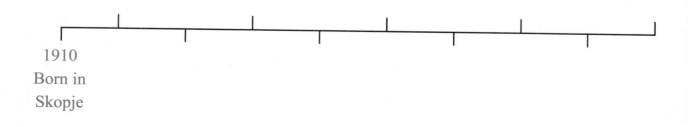

1910
Born in
Skopje

PROBLEM SOLVING

TIME

1. The cricket match was scheduled to begin at 9:45 p.m. Harpreet turned on the TV at 8:20 p.m. How long did she have to wait for the match to start?

   ____

2. The Mathematics test was for 1 hour and 20 minutes. If it got over at 11:15 a.m., when did it begin?

   ____

3. A music CD was played from 4:05 p.m. to 5:20 p.m. How long was the music playing?

   ____

4. Akshay's tennis lessons are 45 minutes long. He started the lesson at 3:40 p.m. It is now 4:15 p.m. How much longer for the lesson to get over?

   ____

5. To prepare for the school sports day which was on 9th October, Aruna started practising from the 11th of September. How many days did she practice? (Note : Do not include Sports Day)

   ____

6. The school annual day was celebrated 3 weeks before Childrens' Day. On which date was it?

   ____

7. A trekking group set off on a trek in the Himalayas on 23rd May. They returned on 15th June. How long was the trek?

   ____

8. Sushi's grandmother started a piece of embroidery on 14th December. She finished it on 3rd March. How long did she take over it? (Take February to have 28 days)

   ____

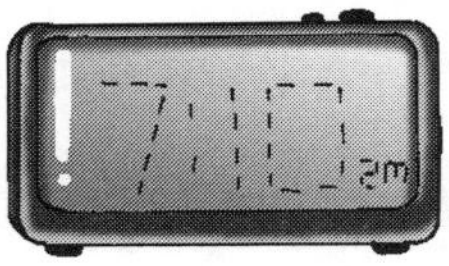

HIGHER ORDER THINKING SKILLS

1. The starting number and the ending number is the same in each of these. Find the numbers.
   (**Hint:** The numbers are less than 8.)

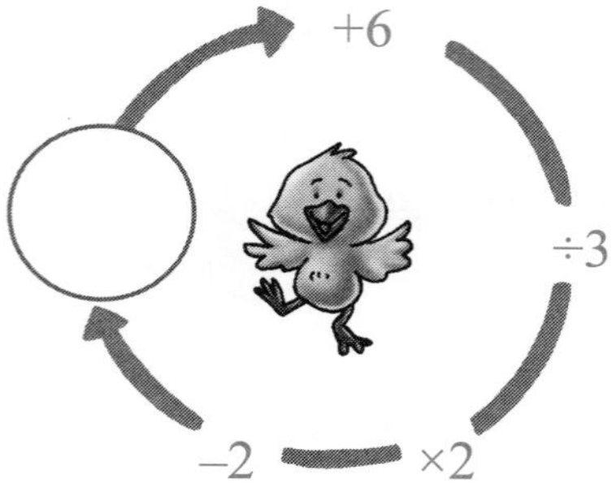

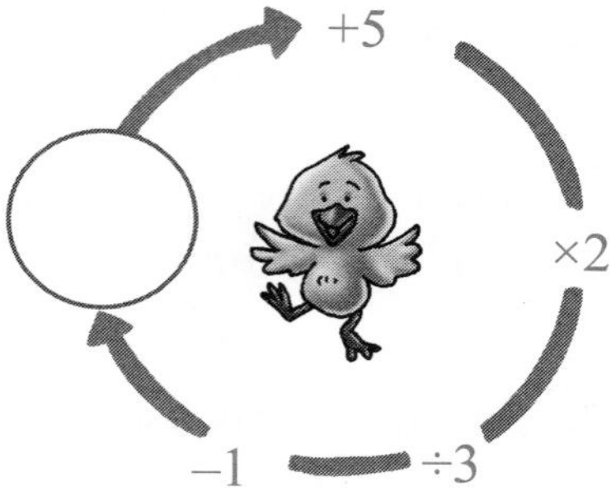

2. What it the smallest number you can add to 123 and get the answer 222?

   ____

3. How many even number pages in a 200 page book?

   ____

4. The fruit seller charges Rs10 for 2 apples or 3 oranges. Will he make more money by selling 30 apples or 36 oranges? How much more?

   ____

5. Which 3 consecutive numbers have a total of 6000?

   ____

6. Shisher celebrated his 9th birthday in 2012. He is five years younger than his brother Shyam. Which year was Shisher born? Which year was Shyam born?

   ____

QUIZ !

1. The school bus comes at 7:05 a.m. Shikha reached the bus stop 10 minutes early. What time did she reach the bus stop? ____________________
2. If I put 50 p everyday in the month of May into my piggy bank, how much money will I have at the end of the month? ____________________
3. It is Friday, 26th April. What is the date next Thursday? ____________________
4. How many months in $2\frac{1}{2}$ years? ____________________
5. If I played for 1 hour 40 minutes and stopped playing at 7:20 p.m., what time did I start playing? ____________________
6. How many days between January 23rd and 23rd February, if you count both days? ______
7. How many hours between 7:00 a.m. and 6 p.m.? ____________________
8. What is the time 30 minutes after 11:30 a.m.? ____________________
9. If school starts at 7:25 a.m. and I reach half an hour early, what time did I reach school? ____________________
10. I started studying at 4:15 p.m. and stopped 2 hours 10 minutes later. What time did I stop studying? ____________________

11. Is it daylight or darkness at 4:15 p.m.? ________________
12. I need 15 minutes to prepare for bed. I go to bed at 9:30 p.m. If it is 8:45 p.m. now, how much more time do I have to read my storybook? ____________________
13. A train is running 45 minutes late and reaches the station at 5:20 p.m. What time would it have reached if it was on time? _______________
14. To travel 500 km in a train, would it take 1 hour, 10 hours or 20 hours?
15. If I exercise for 30 minutes a day, how many hours would I exercise in a week? ____________________
16. How many minutes between 6:15 p.m. and 7:05 p.m.? ____________________
17. How would you write 4:40 p.m. using the 24-hour clock? ____________________
18. Write 20:30 hours using the 12-hour clock. ____________________
19. Is it daylight or darkness at 01: 45 hours? ____________________
20. How many weeks are there in 45 days? ____________________

Handling Data

11

READING A BAR GRAPH

The bar graph below shows the points earned by various houses in a school in the first term. Study the graph and answer the questions.

School House Points (First term)

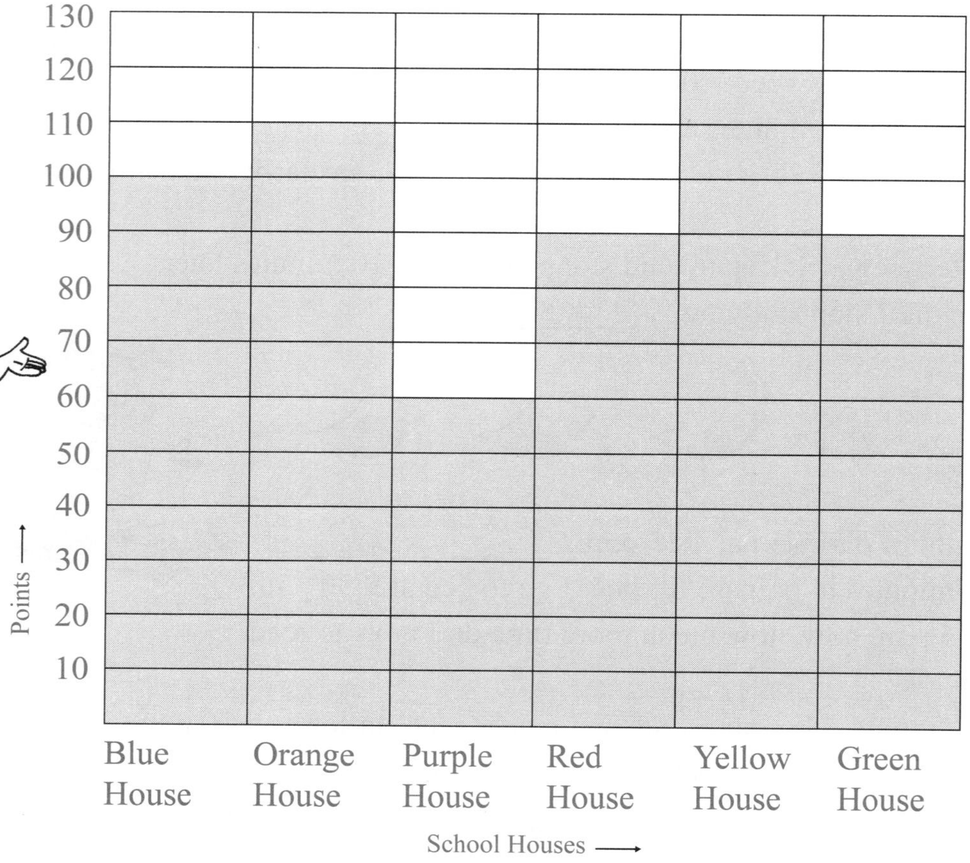

1. How many points has Blue House got so far? ______________
2. Which is the winning house? How many points did it get? ______________
3. Which house has got the least points? How much did it get? ______________
4. Which two houses have got the same number of points? How much did each house get? ______________
5. What is the difference in points between the red house and blue house? ______________
6. Which houses came second and third? ______________
7. Which two houses have a difference of 40 points between them? ______________

PRACTICE WORKSHEET

MAKING A BAR GRAPH

This is a list of the favourite after-dinner dessert of people.

	Name of Dessert	Number of people
1.	Cake	85
2.	Ice cream	90
3.	Halwa	65
4.	Gulab Jamun	70
5.	Fruit Salad	85

Colour the bar graph to show the information. Give the bar graph a title and then answer the questions below.

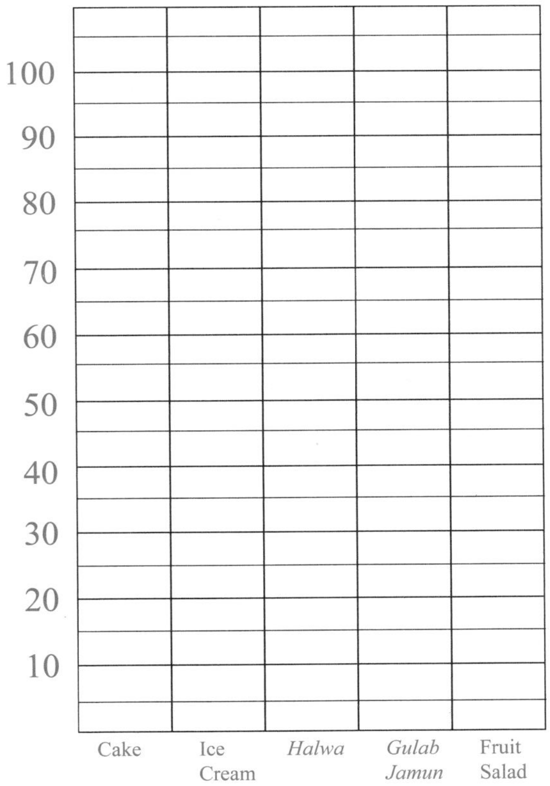

1. How many people in all have been represented in the graph?

____

2. Which is the least popular dessert? How many people like it?

____

3. Which two desserts are equally liked?

____

4. Which is the most favourite dessert of people? How many people have liked it?

____

5. How many more people like ice cream as compared to gulab jamun?

____

CIRCLE GRAPHS

These circle graphs show the collections made by various classes over four weeks for the Prime Minister's Relief Fund. Use the clues to fill in the classes in the circle graphs.

COLLECTIONS II, III, IV

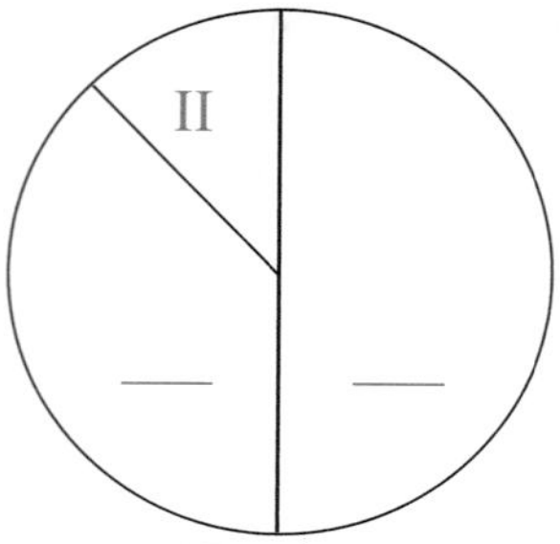

Week-1

Week 1
- Class IV collected the most
- Class II collected the least

COLLECTIONS II, III, IV, V

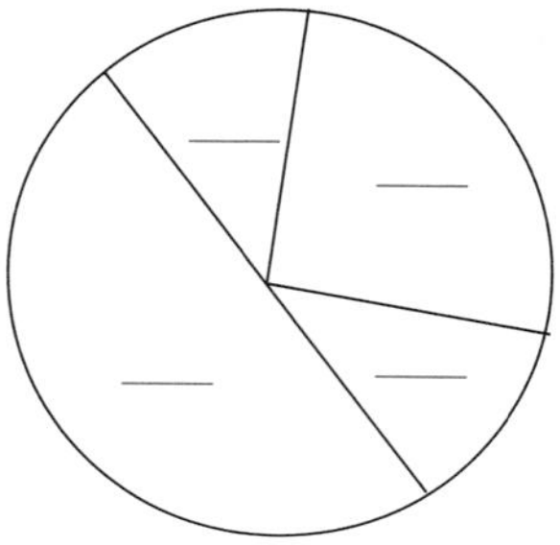

Week-2

Week 2
- Class V collected the most
- Classes III and IV collected the same amount

COLLECTIONS II, III, IV, V

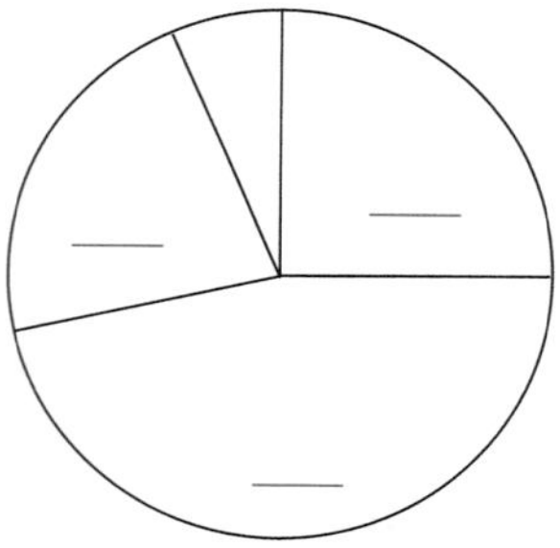

Week-3

Week 3

Class II	$\frac{1}{16}$	Class IV	$\frac{4}{16}$
Class III	$\frac{7}{16}$	Class V	$\frac{4}{16}$

COLLECTIONS II, III, IV, V

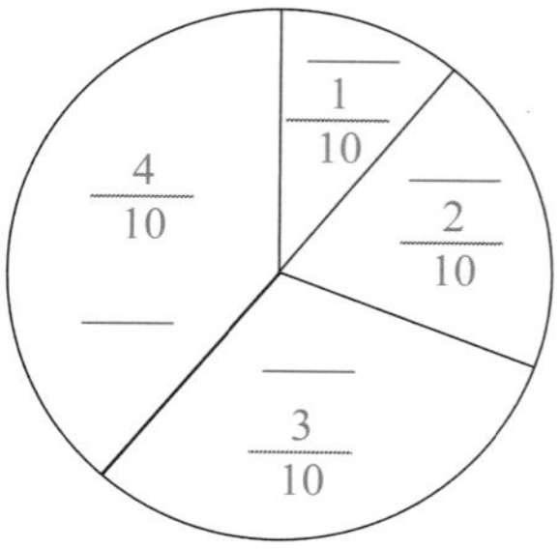

Week-4

Week 4
- Class III collected the least
- Class II collected $\frac{1}{10}$ more than class III
- Class V collected $\frac{1}{10}$ more than class IV

MENTAL MATHS

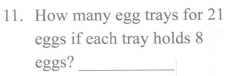

1. Give the difference in the place values of 8 in the number 218865. ____________
2. Write the common factors of 16 and 24. ____________
3. How many 11s in 121? ________
4. What is the product of 4, 5 and 20? ____________
5. 2808 ÷ 100 = Q ____ , R ____
6. Write 7500 paise in rupees. _____
7. Double a number is 48. What is its half ? ____________
8. 10 × 2 years = ____ weeks
9. What is the perimeter of a square with sides 11 cm? ____________
10. $8\frac{1}{4}$ kg = ____ g
11. How many egg trays for 21 eggs if each tray holds 8 eggs? ____________
12. The number after 11199. ___
13. One less than 35070. _______
14. 4764 – ____ = 10
15. 96 + 101 = ____________
16. First three common multiples of 2 and 3. ____________
17. Estimated product of 69 × 71. ____________
18. 78 – 29 = ____
19. Area of a shape covering 32 squares ____________
20. $2\frac{3}{4}$ ℓ = ____mℓ

21. How many minutes are there between 4:45 a.m. and 6:05 a.m.?
22. $\frac{13}{17} + \frac{2}{17}$ = ____________
23. Write $3\frac{1}{11}$ as an improper number.
24. Weight of a computer: 5 ____
25. Water in a vase: 400 ____
26. Length of a saree : 6 ____
27. 136 – 52 + 48 = ____
28. Make the smallest number using 5, 3, 0, 1, 7. ____________
29. Convert $3\frac{1}{2}$ hours into minutes.
30. 10 more than 53990 is ________
31. $\frac{2}{7}$ of 63 = ________________
32. $\frac{11}{19} - \frac{4}{19}$ = ________________
33. Radius of a circle with diameter 140 cm. ____________
34. Weight of a mouse: 20 ____
35. Water in a drum: 500 ____
36. Length of a finger: 5 ____
37. 841 – ____ = 801
38. What is half of 10000?
39. Is 97532 an even number?
40. 320 ÷ 40 = __________

Students may do only 10 sums at a time.

TEST YOUR SKILLS*

Tick the correct answer for each question.

1. What is the time?

(a) 1:20 (b) 3:05
(c) 12:18 (d) 4:05

2. Write 12:05 a.m. using the 24 hour clock.
(a) 12:05 hrs
(b) 22:05 hrs
(c) 00:05 hrs
(d) 02:05 hrs

3. Write 22:45 hours using the 12 hour clock.
(a) 12:45 p.m.
(b) 10:45 p.m.
(c) 12:45 a.m.
(d) 10:45 a.m.

4. How much time has passed from 3:30 p.m. to 8:55 p.m.?
(a) 5 hrs 25 min
(b) 5 hrs 15 min
(c) 6 hrs 15 min
(d) 4 hrs 25 min

5. How many days from March 13 to April 2? (Include both days.)
(a) 19 days
(b) 20 days
(c) 21 days
(d) 22 days

6. Ashish practiced maths sums for an hour and 20 minutes. If he started at 4:45pm, when did he finish?
(a) 6:05 p.m. (b) 5:05 p.m.
(c) 6:15 p.m. (d) 6:05 a.m.

7. Seema finishes her music class at 7:30 p.m. If her class was 45 minutes long, when did she begin the class?
(a) 1:15 p.m. (b) 6:45 a.m.
(c) 5:45 p.m. (d) 6:45 p.m.

8. What will be the time 4 hours after 9:15 a.m.?
(a) 1:15 p.m.
(b) 2:15 a.m.
(c) 12:15 p.m.
(d) 1:15 a.m.

9. Hobbies Class IV

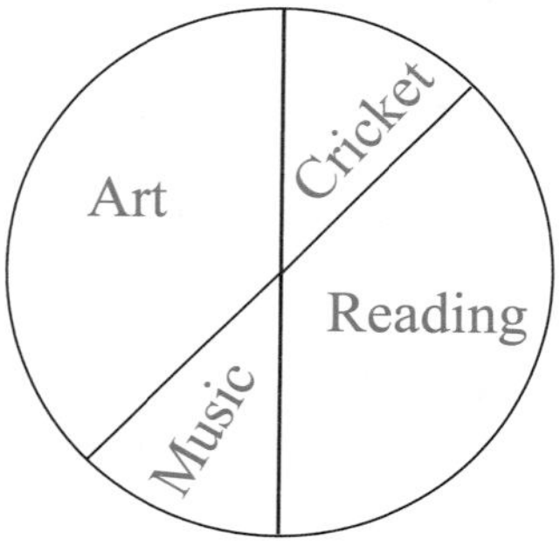

It there are 40 children in the class, how many children have art and music as a hobby ?
(a) 25 children
(b) 20 children
(c) 10 children
(d) 15 children

10. Favourite TV Channels

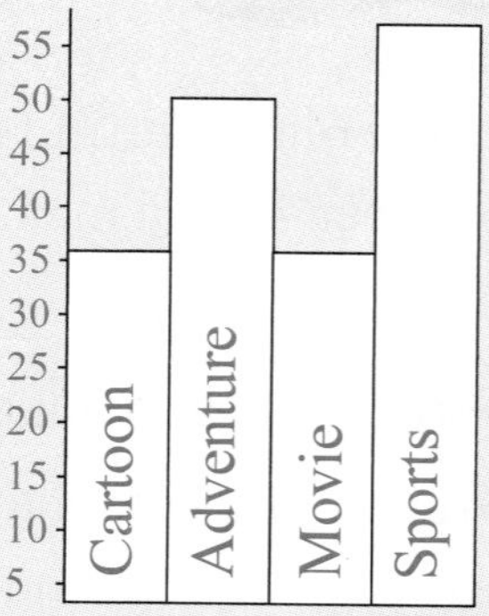

From the bar graph above, find how many like adventure channels the best?
(a) 25 people
(b) 35 people
(c) 40 people
(d) 50 people

*This is for chapters 10,11.

ANSWERS TO SELECT QUESTIONS

Page 8

(a) 97521, 12579 **(e)** 7753, 3357
(b) 86320, 20368 **(f)** 8820, 2008
(c) 88761, 11678 **(g)** 99942, 22249
(d) 55320, 20035 **(h)** 99980, 80009

Page 11

1. 10th floor **2.** 3+1;2+2;1+3 **3.** 71
4. 10 and 8 **5.** 15 and 6

Page 18

2. Pink-408.75, Blue-392.50, Rs 16.25
3. Nose-636.25, Neck-349.75, Rs 286.50
4. Earth-719.50, Water-559.25, Rs 160.25
5. Snake-639.50, Snail -767.75, Rs 128.25
6. Hockey-862.75, Tennis-739.25, Rs 123.50
7. Pencil-712.00, Eraser-885.25, Rs 173.25

Page 19

1. 167 bookmarks **2.** 480 candles
3. Rs 372 **4.** Rs 12,750 **5.** 285 seats

Page 23

1. 5760	**2.** 19600	**3.** 43380	**4.** 51960
5. 13170	**6.** 21640	**7.** 45780	**8.** 29250
9. 8240	**10.** 31500	**11.** 10000	**12.** 35300
13. 75760	**14.** 249760	**15.** 770480	**16.** 55720
17. 102800	**18.** 268740	**19.** 788850	**20.** 138510
21. 210520	**22.** 506080	**23.** 708480	**24.** 418080

Page 24

1. 15870	**2.** 28792	**3.** 12411	**4.** 28875
5. 18011	**6.** 26675	**7.** 23458	**8.** 53400
9. 69388	**10.** 48389	**11.** 34577	**12.** 42693
13. 36077	**14.** 66164	**15.** 43065	**16.** 12816
17. 38458	**18.** 36868	**19.** 66748	**20.** 51743
21. 32292	**22.** 53037	**23.** 56883	**24.** 24375
25. 39903	**26.** 26388	**27.** 45308	**28.** 57270

Page 25

1. 41500	**2.** 329094	**3.** 578144	**4.** 252800
5. 251835	**6.** 93174	**7.** 258060	**8.** 55118
9. 452574	**10.** 134415	**11.** 190518	**12.** 306768

Page 27

1. Rs 105.75 **2.** Watch **3.** Rs 390 **4.** Rs 470.75
5. Rs 24.50 **6.** Rs 228.50

Page 28

1-e 2-a 3-d 4-f 5-b 6-d

Page 29

1. Add **2.** Divide **3.** Multiply **4.** Subtract
5. Multiply **6.** Subtract **7.** Divide

Page 30

1. 6 biscuits **2.** Rs 97.00 **3.** 212 books
4. 144 packets **5.** 342 children

Page 32

1. b	**2.** b	**3.** d	**4.** c
5. a	**6.** d	**7.** a	**8.** b
9. d	**10.** a	**11.** c	**12.** b

Page 33

1. 1241 **2.** 1283 **3.** 2156 **4.** 1711
5. 1108 **6.** 1162 **7.** 1211 **8.** 1111
9. Q = 1793, R = 1 **10.** Q = 1244, R = 2
11. Q = 2215, R = 1 **12.** Q = 1515, R = 3
13. Q = 1140, R = 1 **14.** Q = 1319, R = 5
15. Q = 1114, R = 2 **16.** Q = 1102, R = 2

Page 36

1. Q = 32, R = 0 **2.** Q = 2, R = 0 **3.** Q = 9, R = 0 **4.** Q = 22, R = 5
5. Q = 13, R = 2 **6.** Q = 3, R = 0 **7.** Q = 20, R = 18 **8.** Q = 7, R = 3
9. Q = 6, R = 8 **10.** Q = 8, R = 0 **11.** Q = 14, R = 7 **12.** Q = 31, R = 0
13. Q = 15, R = 0

Page 38

1. 17 cartons **2.** 9 teams **3.** 8 pictures **4.** 7 supervisors
5. 7 ice-creams, Rs 6 **6.** 10 tables

Page 39

1. (b) 151 women **2.** (a) 819 people
3. (c) 6250 saplings **4.** (b) 173 km
5. (a) Rs 8120

Page 40

1. (a) Rs 12.25 (b) Rs 11.95
(c) Rs 28.50 (d) Rs 15.00
(e) Rs 13.50
2. (a) Rs 36.75 (b) Rs 121.50
(c) Rs 142.50 (d) Rs 23.90
(e) Rs 90

Page 41

1. Rs 6328 **2.** Rs 4168 **3.** Rs 10,575 **4.** 1236
5. Rs 895 **6.** Rs 795 **7.** Rs 3,412

Page 42

1. Rs 1211 **2.** 8 toffees and 9 chocolates
3. Lost Rs 2 **4.** Rs 500
5. 3 coins of Rs 5, one coin of Rs 2 and one coin of Re 1

Page 48

2. 7.45 a.m. **3.** (a) 67 (b) 42
4. Rs 9, Rs 6

Page 49

1. 1 **2.** False **3.** 7
4. 100,200,300,400,500 **5.** False **6.** Yes
7. 2 **8.** 1 **9.** 3 **10.** No
11. False **12.** No **13.** 1 **14.** False
15. 20, 40 **16.** True **17.** 1 and 3 **18.** True
19. 1,5,25 **20.** 14, 49

Page 54

1. (a) 2 (b) 4 (c) 6 (d) 8 **2.** (a) 10 (b) 9 (c) 8 (d) 7
3. (a) 12 (b) 13 (c) 14 (d) 15 **4.** (a)10 (b)20 (c)30 (d) 40
5. (a) 10 (b) 15 (c) 20 (d) 25 **6.** (a) 12 (b) 9 (c) 6 (d) 3
7. (a) 4 (b) 8 (c) 16 (d) 32 **8.** (a)40 (b)20 (c)10 (d) 5

Page 55

1. (a) $3\frac{3}{6}$ (b) $3\frac{2}{7}$ (c) $4\frac{2}{6}$ (d) $2\frac{3}{8}$
(e) 3 (f) $1\frac{4}{7}$ (g) $2\frac{3}{4}$ (h) $1\frac{2}{8}$
(i) 2 (j) $5\frac{1}{3}$ (k) $3\frac{2}{8}$ (l) $8\frac{2}{3}$
(m) $4\frac{4}{8}$ (n) $4\frac{1}{6}$ (o) $2\frac{6}{9}$ (p) $2\frac{2}{5}$
(q) $1\frac{5}{10}$ (r) $5\frac{2}{6}$ (s) 7 (t) $4\frac{2}{4}$
2. (a) $\frac{5}{3}$ (b) $\frac{9}{4}$ (c) $\frac{13}{8}$ (d) $\frac{7}{3}$
(e) $\frac{21}{5}$ (f) $\frac{7}{2}$ (g) $\frac{13}{5}$ (h) $\frac{7}{5}$
(i) $\frac{27}{8}$ (j) $\frac{31}{7}$ (k) $\frac{23}{7}$ (l) $\frac{30}{9}$
(m) $\frac{11}{9}$ (n) $\frac{41}{7}$ (o) $\frac{11}{8}$ (p) $\frac{23}{5}$
(q) $\frac{17}{7}$ (r) $\frac{4}{3}$ (s) $\frac{28}{5}$ (t) $\frac{20}{9}$

Page 56

1. 9 kg **2.** 12 minutes **3.** 42 kg **4.** $\frac{3}{5}$th
5. 50 elephants **6.** 3 moons **7.** 4 years

Page 57

1. No, because $\frac{4}{9}+\frac{7}{9} > 1$ bag
2. No, as the total number of books carried by Amin, Mina and Purva is more than 12.
3. Yes, because half of 12 is less than half of 18
4. No, as going back would also consume same fuel.
5. Yes, because some children might be wearing spectacles.
6. Yes, Shikha's apple may be bigger.
7. Yes, their time overlapped with each other.
8. Yes, because one half equals 2 quarters.

Page 58

1. (a) Fraction A = $\frac{3}{5}$ (b) Fraction C = $\frac{3}{7}$
Fraction B = $\frac{1}{5}$ Fraction D = $\frac{2}{7}$
2. 3 yellow tricycles **3.** (a) $\frac{8}{27}$ (b) $\frac{12}{27}$ (c) $\frac{6}{27}$ (d) $\frac{1}{27}$
4. 9 hurdles for 100 m, 19 hurdles for 200 m

Page 60

1. c **2.** c **3.** b **4.** b
5. c **6.** b **7.** b **8.** a
9. d **10.** d **11.** a **12.** b

Page 65

3. Rectangles = 9
Triangles = 12
4. a,b,c,e
5. (a) T (b) F (c) T (d) T (e) F

Page 69

1. 250 m **2.** 100 m **3.** 250 cm **4.** 25 cm
5. 21 m **6.** 125 cm **7.** 99 m

Page 70

1. 200 g less **2.** 2 kg will cost Rs 36, half kilo will cost Rs 9
3. 500 g **4.** 5 packets **5.** 2500 g
6. 20 tea bags **7.** $3\frac{1}{4}$kg

Page 71

1. 525 mℓ **2.** 10 mℓ more **3.** 515 mℓ
4. $\frac{1}{2}$ ℓ grape juice and 1ℓ apple juice
5. 10 Oranges **6.** c,e,f,g,h

Page 73

1. 3×3 = 9 2×4 =8, 5×5 = 25 4×6 = 24
2. 256 m **3.** 4 days **4.** 430 mℓ **5.** 250 m
6. 370 g **7.** 175 cm

Page 76

1. (a) 83 m (b) 136 cm (c) 108 m (d) 92 m
(e) 142 cm (f) 116 m (g) 164 m (h) 100 cm
(i) 65 m
2. (a) 7 m (b) 5 cm (c) 3 cm (d) 5 cm
(e) 12 m (f) 6 m

Page 79

1. 1 km 400 m **2.** 600 m **3.** 4 cm
4. 15 cm **5.** (a) 150 km (b) 325 km (c) 435 km
(d) Spotless Town

Page 80

1. 22 titles **2.** both are same

4.
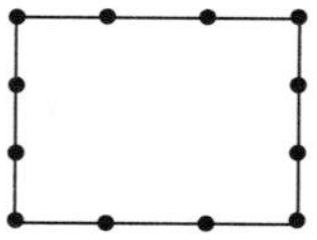

5. One of many solutions
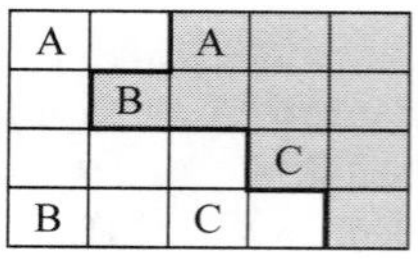

Page 82

1. a **2.** c **3.** b **4.** c
5. b **6.** a **7.** a **8.** d
9. b **10.** b **11.** a **12.** c

Page 87

1. 1 hr 25 min **2.** 9:55 a.m. **3.** 1 hr 15 min
4. 10 min **5.** 28 days **6.** 25th October
7. 24 days **8.** 80 days

Page 89

1. 6:55 a.m. **2.** Rs 15.50 **3.** 2nd May **4.** 30 months
5. 5: 40 p.m. **6.** 32 days **7.** 11 hours **8.** 12 noon
9. 6:55 a.m. **10.** 6.25 p.m. **11.** day light **12.** 30 min
13. 4.35 p.m. **14.** 10 hours **15.** $3\frac{1}{2}$ hrs
16. 50 min **17.** 16: 40 hours **18.** 8.30 p.m.
19. darkness **20.** 6 weeks

Page 94

1. d **2.** c **3.** b **4.** a
5. c **6.** a **7.** d **8.** a
9. b **10.** d